KAMA SUTRA

VATSYAYANA

KAMA SUTRA

THE HINDU RITUAL OF LOVE

CASTLE BOOKS — NEW YORK

Distributed to the Trade by
BOOK SALES, INC.
352 Park Avenue South
New York 10, N.Y.

CONTENTS

of

KAMA SUTRA

PART SEVEN

SEDUCTION

PART ONE

*Observations on the three necessities for
Happiness on Earth - Virtue, Riches and
Pleasure. A Conversation*

MASTER: The span of human life is about 100 years, and during
this time a man must practice Dharma, Artha and Kama, in
such a way that his whole existence achieves a perfect balance.

During childhood his principal object should be to acquire
education. In youth and maturity, Artha and Kama should be
his main pursuits, while age brings a dedication to Dharma
in an effort to achieve Moksha and halt the wheel of reincarna-
tion. However, due to the uncertainty of human existence, a
wise man should practice all three principles at any stage of
his life that is appropriate. But one important principle must
be maintained. A youth should live the life of a seminarist
until he has completed his education. What are these three
principles of human existence?

Dharma is obedience to the Shastras, or Holy Scriptures,
which recommend the performance of certan rites and sacrifices. These rituals are often neglected because they relate   to
another existence and therefore seem less real as their effects are
not visible. The Shastras also forbid the eating of meat, but this
commandment is more easily followed, as meat is something
material and visible. Dharma is instructed by the Shruti (Holy
Scriptures) and by those who explain and interpret it.

Artha is the acquisition of lands, cattle, riches, followers,
friends, and proficiency in the arts. It also implies the protection
of that which is acquired and the acquisition of that which is
protected. Artha is taught by the King's officers, and by merchants
experienced in commerce.

Kama is the enjoyment of material things through the
medium of the senses—hearing, touch, sight, taste and smell.

9

The basic definition of Kama is the special contact between the sensory organ and its object, and the resulting pleasure is known as Kama. Kama is taught by the Kama Sutras (verses of desire) and by experience. However, it may be said that when the three great principles of human existence are united, Dharma is more meritorious than Artha; and Artha than Kama. But Artha, for example, should always be practised by a King, for on Artha alone depends the welfare of his people. In the same way, Kama should be the principal preoccupation of courtesans, as their occupation and livelihood depend on their understanding of its principles.

STUDENT: The ancient sages have said that as Dharma is concerned with things not of this world, its principles can be adequately defined and treated in a book. The same is true of Artha, because its successful practice is possible by the application of certain principles which can only be learnt through study and reading. But Kama, which is a part of nature itself, does not need to be studied.

MASTER: That is not altogether true. Sexual relationships are dependent on a man and a woman, and to develop such a relationship requires the application of certain methods, outlined in the Kama Shastras. The lack of these special techniques among, for instance, the animals of the jungle, is due to the fact that these animals have no need to practise restraint. The females only desire sexual intercourse during specific seasons, and their encounter is not preceded or conditioned by any intellectual process.

STUDENT: The Lokayatikas say that it is useless to follow religious precepts in the hope of a future reward, because one can never be sure if, indeed, such a reward exists. Who would be so foolish as to let what he possesses slip into the hands of others? Moreover, as the saying goes, it is preferable to possess a pigeon today than a peacock tomorrow; a cup of brass that one is certain of obtaining is better than the promise of a golden goblet.

MASTER: That is not so.

1) The Holy Scriptures recommend the practice of Dharma and does not allow of doubt.

2) The sacrifices one offers for the downfall of one's enemies or for rain have a visible result.

3) The sun, the moon, the stars, the planets and other celestial bodies seem to function in a regulated way for the good of the world.

4) The order and continuation of human society is assured

by the observation of rules concerning the four classes of men and the four stages of human life.

5) We see that seeds are sown in the ground in the hope of a future harvest.

STUDENT: Those who believe that Destiny is the prime motivator of all things say: One must not struggle to acquire wealth because sometimes despite all our work and efforts, we remain poor; while others accumulate a fortune without any effort on their part. Consequently everything is conditioned by Destiny, which is the supreme master of gain and loss, success and disaster, pleasure and pain. Thus we have seen the Demona Bali raised to the throne of Indra by Destiny and dethroned by the same power, and it is through Destiny alone that one can again restore his fortunes.

MASTER: This is false reasoning. As the acquisition of any object presupposes a certain effort on the part of man, the application of certain techniques can be considered as the 'cause' of certain acquisitions. These techniques being normally necessary, even when some event is predestined, it follows that a person who makes no effort derives no satisfaction or happiness from his gains.

STUDENT: Those who are inclined to believe in Artha as the principle virtue reason that man should not seek pleasures, because it is an obstacle to the practice of Dharma and Artha, both of which are superior in merit to Kama, and indulgence in pleasures is despised by virtuous people. Pleasure leads man to unhappiness and ultimate dissatisfaction and brings him into contact with unworthy persons. It also leads him to commit acts of impurity and inspires in him a recklessness as regards the future and encourages dissipation, frivolity and weakness. It it well known, too, that many men who are devoted exclusively to the pursuit of pleasure ruin themselves and their families and friends. Thus the King Dandakya, who kidnapped and raped the daughter of a Brahmin, was cursed by the latter and his whole kingdom was buried in an avalanche of sand. Indra, who violated the chastity of Ahalya, was cursed by her husband, Gautama, and found his body covered with festering sores. Also the powerful Kichaka, who tried to seduce Draupadi, and Ravenna, who abducted Sita, were both severely punished for their crimes. These kings and many others were the victims of their desire for pleasure.

MASTER: This objection is not valid, as pleasures are not necessary as food for the healthy sustenance of the body, and are therefore quite acceptable. Moreover pleasure is a direct result of Dharma

11

and Artha. Besides, moderation and prudence should always accompany the pursuit of pleasure. No one refrains from cooking food because there are beggars who may steal it; nor ceases to sow seed because there are animals who may destroy the grain when it ripens. Thus a man who practices Dharma, Artha and Kama tastes happiness—both in this life and the next. People usually practice only those things that do not compromise the future and which do not harm their welfare. Any act which ultimately leads to the practice of Dharma, Artha and Kama, united or separately, should be encouraged. But the prudent man will refrain from the performance of any acts which will lead to the fulfillment of one of these principles at the expense of the other two.

CHAPTER 2

The Study of the sixty-four Arts

A man should study the *Kama Sutra* and the arts and sciences which are auxiliary to it, as well as the arts and sciences which lead to a deeper understanding of Dharma and Artha.

Young virgins should also study the *Kama Sutra* and the accompanying arts and sciences before their marriage, and they should continue this study after their nuptials with the permission of their husbands.

Many sages, however, disagree on this point, for there is an ancient law which forbids the study of the sciences to women; and therefore many scholars think that the study of the *Kama Sutra* should also be banned.

But Vatsyayana does not believe that this objection is valid, as many women are already wise in the practices of the *Kama Sutra*, which derives its tenets from the *Kama Shastras*, or the science of love itself. Moreover, this is not the only case where the practical application of a certain science is known to all, while the actual principles and laws on which the science is based are known only to a handful of sages and scholars. Thus the *Yadnikas*—sacrificial priests—though completely illiterate and quite ignorant of grammar are able to employ the appropriate words to invoke the different Gods. And many people fulfill all the requisite ceremonies on certain propitious days fixed by the astrologers, though they may know nothing about astrology themselves. In the same way, trainers of horses and the mahouts of elephants, though they never study the art of taming animals, manage to acquire control over their beasts through trial, error, and constant practice. Likewise, citizens living in distant provinces obey the laws of the kingdom for no better reason than that they have always done so and it has become a habit, and also perhaps because there is a king over them.

Every man knows from experience that certain women, such as the daughters of princes and of ministers and courtesans, are well versed in the subtle practices of the *Kama Shastras.*

A woman, consequently, must learn the *Kama Shastra,* or at least some parts of it, by studying their practical application under the guidance of a close and intimate friend. But she should study alone and by herself the sixty-four arts that can be said to form a part of the shastras. Those who instruct her in the practices of the *Kama Shastra* should be married women who are either:

1) The daughter of her nurse who has been brought up with her;—2) A trustworthy friend, or her maternal aunt;—3) An old servant or a beggar woman who has previously known and lived with the family;—4) Or her own sister, whom she can always trust.

And she should acquire the following arts through diligent study along with a practical knowledge of the *Kama Shastra:*

1) Singing;—2) A musical instrument;—3) Dancing;—4) The association of dance, song and music;—5) Caligraphy and drawing; —6) Tattooing;—7) The correct decoration of an idol with rice and flowers;—8) The arrangement of flowers—9) The science of dyeing and coloring cloth and parts of the body, such as the hair, the nails and the lips;—10) Glass moasaics;—11) The art of bed-making and arranging carpets and cushions in the most comfortable way;—12) How to play musical water bowls;—13) The drainage and storage of water in aqueducts, cisterns and reservoirs;—14) Painting, decoration and arrangement;—15) How to make prayer beads, necklaces, garlands and coronets;—16) The art of making turbans and belts from flowers and aigrettes;—17) The theatrical arts and the production of dramatic representations; —18) The art of designing earrings;—19) The mixing and preparation of perfumes;—20) The art of dressing and the tasteful arrangement of jewels and ornaments;—21) Magic or sorcery;— 22) Sleight of hand and illusionism;—23) The art of cooking;—24) The preparation of sherbets, fruit juices and alcoholic drinks with

the appropriate essences and coloring;—25) The art of cutting and sewing ;—26) The confection of parrots, flowers, bouquets, balls, etc. out of wool and silk;—27) The solution of riddles, puzzles, conundrums and enigmatic questions;—28) A game which consists in reciting verses: when one person has finished reciting a verse, the next player must immediately begin another verse in which the first word must begin with the last letter of the previous verse; if a player cannot immediately think of a verse, he is considered the loser and must pay a forfeit;—29) The art of mimicry and imitation;—30) Reading aloud and traditional chants and intonations;—31) The study of phrases difficult to pronounce. This a game much loved by women and children; the player has to repeat a difficult phrase very rapidly, taking care not to confuse or mispronounce the words;—32) Knowledge of fencing, staff and quarter staff and of the bow and arrow;—33) The art of logical reasoning;—34) Carpentry;—35) Architecture;—36) The ability to judge pieces of gold, silver, precious stones and jewels;—37) Chemistry and mineralogy;—38) The coloring of stones, jewels and pearls;—39) The knowledge of mines and collieries;—40) Gardening; the art of curing illness with herbs and plants, and a detailed knowledge of how to grow and tend these herbs;—41) The rules of cock fighting and ram combats;—43) The art of teaching parrots to talk;—43) The art of applying perfumes to the body and of impregnating the hair with pomades and scents;—44) A profound knowledge of letters and characters and the ability to write words in different forms;—45) The art of speaking and changing the form of words. There are various ways of doing this: some change the beginning and end of words, others insert certain letters between each syllable of a word;—46) A knowledge of languages and provincial dialects;—47) The art of decorating a chariot with flowers for religious and festive ceremonies;—48) The art of drawing mystic diagrams, preparing charms, incantations and of weaving protective bracelets;—49) Intellectual exercises, such as completing the verses of a poem, or making a poem out of various verses chosen at random, or improving a poem in which the meter is not quite correct by adding or eliminating vowels or consonants, or rendering in prose or verse the meaning of signs and symbols;—50) The writing of poetry;—51) The knowledge of dictionaries and vocabularies;—52) The art of disguising or changing the appearance of people;—53) The art of tasteful illusion, such as disguising cotton as silk and making crude and cheap objects appear delicate and beautiful;—54) Different kinds of games;—55) Self-purification through prayers and mystic incantations;—56) The ability to partake in juvenile sports;—57) The knowledge of social usage; how to pay a compliment and the correct forms of address;—58) The science of war, arms and armies;—59) Gymnastics;—60) The ability to judge the character of a man by studying his face;—61) The art of scanning verses;—62) Mathematical recreations;—63) The art of making artificial flowers;—64) The molding of figures and images in potter's clay.

A courtesan who has a good disposition and who is versed in the above-mentioned arts, receives the title of *Ganika* or a courtesan of high quality, and she is entitled to a chair of honor in masculine society. She is universally respected and her favors are sought by all. The King seeks her out and the sages sing her praises. In the same way, the wife of a King, as well as that of a minister, who is proficient in these arts can be sure that she will have precedence in her husband's esteem, even though he may frequent thousands of other women. Add to these advantages the case of the woman who 'divorces' her husband, for if she is well versed in the above arts, she can always earn her own living even in a foreign land.

The theoretical knowledge alone of these arts is of great value to a woman, as their practical application often depends on circumstances.

Moreover, a man who is also versed in these arts and who is eloquent and well versed in the subtle traditions of gallantry, easily and swiftly conquers feminine hearts.

CHAPTER 3

The life of the Citizen; his house, daily duties, amusements and companions

A man who is educated and who possesses a fortune—either inherited or gained; through gifts if he is a Brahmin, by conquest if he is of the Kshatrya caste, and by commerce or other such means if he is a Vaishya—should become the head of a household and live the life of a useful citizen.

He should choose to live in a town or a large village, or in an honest neighborhood, or in some crowded locality. His house should be situated near running water and should be divided into diverse sections for different uses. The dwelling should be surrounded by a garden and should contain two apartments, an exterior and an interior one. The inner apartment should be reserved for the women of the house. The exterior one should be richly perfumed and should contain a huge soft bed covered with a spotless white sheet, slightly raised towards the center and surrounded by garlands and bowls of flowers. The bed should be covered by a canopy overhead, and there should be two pillows, one for the head and one for the foot. The room should also contain a sofa, and above this there should be a small shelf to hold the perfumed ointments for the night, flowers, pots of collyre and other perfumes used to freshen the breath, as well as several lemon peels. On the floor near the sofa there should always be a brass spittoon, a jewel box, a lute hung on an elephant tusk, a drawing table, perfumes, some books and garlands of yellow amaranth. The room should also contain a round seat, a box of games and a dice table. In the outer apartment there should be a cage for birds, and a separate little room should be kept for sculpturing and fashioning wood and other such diversions. In the garden there should be a revolving swing as well as an ordinary one, also a summer house and benches to sit on. In the morning, the head of the house, after he has done his indispensable duties, must wash his teeth, apply moderate quantities of perfumes and oils to his body, put mascara on his lids and eyes, and color his lips with alacktaka, and then study the whole effect carefully in the mirror. Then, having chewed some 'pan' and other such things that freshen the breath and sweeten the taste in the mouth, he should go about his daily duties.

He should take a bath every day. Every second day he should anoint his body with oil; every third day he should rub a foamy substance on his body; every fourth day he should shave his face and head, and every fifth or tenth day the other parts of his body.

All these bodily functions should be performed punctually and he should take special care to wash under his armpits.

He should eat three times a day—in the morning, at midday and in the evening as prescribed by hayrayana.

After breakfast he should teach his parrots and other birds to talk. Later he should prepare his fighting cocks, partridges and rams for combat, and also devote some of his time to dramatic spectacles and various other entertainments with the Pitharmadas, the Vitas and the Vidushakas. After lunch he should sleep for an hour and then spend the afternoon conversing with his friends.

The evening should begin with song. Then the head of the household should retire to his perfumed chamber with a friend and await the arrival of the woman who loves him, who may send him a messenger or who may come herself to find him. When she finally arrives, the head of the house and his friend should welcome her and pass the hours of the evening in amusing conversation until desire slowly comes upon them. Then the lord of the house should dismiss his friend and so fulfill his last task of the day.

Here are some entertainments and amusements that enliven the life of the honest citizen:

1) Festivals; — 2) Gatherings and parties where both sexes are present; — 3) Drinking bouts; — 4) Picnics; — 5) Other social entertainments.

Festivals

On a certain propitious day, the citizens of the town should gather in the Temple of Sarasvati. This festival is dedicated to the arts. Singers and other artists come together on this day to present their new songs and to demonstrate their talents. The next day prizes are awarded to the deserving artists.

During festivals, the townsfolk should share all the expenses and always make decisions and help each other both in times of prosperity and in the lean years. It is the duty of every citizen to offer hospitality to any stranger who may have come to the feast. These rules, naturally, hold true for any other feasts that may be celebrated in praise of other Gods.

Gatherings and Parties

A social gathering is an assembly where men of the same age, education and dispositions, who enjoy the same things meet and invite some courtesans to a public hall or to the home of one of the assembly, and spend the evening in pleasant conversation.

The guests spend the evening composing poems and completing verses begun by others, and testing each other's knowledge in the various arts and sciences.

Women who are famous for their beauty and who possess the same talents, education and tastes as these men are very popular and are also highly honored at such gatherings.

Drinking Bouts

Men and women should only hold drinking parties privately in each other's homes.

At these parties the men should invite the courtesans to drink

17

with them such bitter and intoxicating liquors as Madhou, Aireya, Sara and Asawa, as well as other drinks made out of the barks of various trees, or from fruit and wild plants.

Picnics

In the mornings, after they have washed and dressed, the men should go for a morning ride on horseback in the gardens accompanied by courtesans and their servants.

There they should engage in physical exercises, tests of strength and other diversions, such as cock fights and combats of partridges and rams, and after they have pleasantly passed the morning, they should return home in the afternoon carrying bouquets of flowers that they have gathered.

In the same way they may swim in a pond which has been previously cleaned and emptied of all dangerous animals or harmful plants.

Other Social Entertainments

Other social diversions include: Spending the night playing dice; —Walking in the moonlight;—Celebrating a spring festival;—Picking mango buds and fruit;—Eating lotus seeds and the soft kernel of corn;

Holding picnics in the forests when the trees are dressed in their tender new green foliage;

Udakakshvedika, or exercises in water;—Disguising each other in leaves;—A battle of flowers with the blooms of the Kadamba tree, and a host of other sports, diversions and amusements that are appropriate to the country, province or region.

These pleasures are usually enjoyed either by a man alone with his chosen courtesans, or by a courtesan who is out with a group of men.

Other companions are the *Pithamardas, Vitas* and *Vidushakas.*

Pithamarda is a man without fortune whose sole possessions in life are his Mallike—a chair in the form of a *T*—some foamy soapy substance, and a red costume. He comes from a renowned part of the province and is well versed in all the arts. In fact it is as a sort of teacher in these arts that he is invited to the homes of citizens and their courtesans.

Vita is a man who enjoys the advantages of a comfortable income. He is usually a compatriot of the citizens with whom he is so friendly, possesses his own house, servants and women, and is honored as a companion in the homes of the citizens and courtesans who also provide him with his income.

Vidushaka, also called *Vaihasaka,* which means 'one who causes laughter,' is not only a man who is adroit in certain arts, but one who is also reputed to be amusing and is therefore tolerated in gay circles.

These different persons can also act as mediators in quarrels and effect reconciliations between citizens and their courtesans. Beggars, women with shaved heads, adulteresses and old courtesans accomplished in the arts of love, can also serve the same functions.

Thus a citizen who lives in a town or in a village, and who is respected by all, mixes freely with members of his caste who for one reason or another are desirable. He should converse with them daily and also present them to his friends, and by doing them small favors he will win their loyalty and oblige them to return these favors when he needs any services.

A citizen who can wisely discourse with his friends
In many tongues, not only Sanskrit, and his native dialect
Wins the respect and admiration of the company.
The wise man should never mix with a group despised,
A group that scorns the rules of society
And tends to destroy the structure of other companies;
But a wise man whose friends respect tradition
And who is admired by one and all
And whose one object in life is the full enjoyment of pleasure
Is highly respected by all the peoples of the world.

CHAPTER 4

Women with whom intercourse is either permitted or forbidden. Friends and intermediaries

If any man belonging to one of the four castes desires to enter into union with a virgin belonging to his own caste according to the laws of the Holy Scriptures (that is to say in legal marriage), this union provides a means of acquiring a legitimate succession and of preserving a good reputation. Moreover, such a union is in perfect harmony with the normal practices of society.

On the other hand, intercourse with women of a higher caste, or with those already wise in the ways of love, is strictly prohibited.

But intercourse with women of inferior castes, with women expelled from their own society, with courtesans and with 'twice married' women* is neither recommended nor forbidden. For pleasure is the only objective of a union with such women.

And all such women as may be enjoyed without sin or shame are known as *Nayikas*.

There are generally three kinds of *Nayikas*: virgins, twice married women, and courtesans.

Yet the sage Gonikaputra is of the opinion that there exists yet a fourth kind of Nayika with whom a man may enter into a relationship for very special reasons, even though she be married to another. The reasons which allow him to violate the sanctity of marriage with impunity are the following:

1) The woman is willing and many others have enjoyed her before him. Consequently, she may be regarded as a kind of courtesan, and a man has a perfect right to his pleasure with her, even if such a woman belongs to a higher caste.

2) If such a woman has left her legal husband and is living as the wife of another.

3) If this woman has won the love of her rich and powerful husband, and is able to influence him. If this husband is the friend of your enemy, then as a result of your liaison, this woman may persuade her husband to abandon your enemy.

4) She might be able to prevent her husband, who has always disliked you, from harming you.

5) Or again, if you win the love of such a woman, you may be able to kill her powerful husband and so indirectly acquire his immense wealth.

6) Or again if you are poor, union with such a woman may bring you both money and influence.

7) Perhaps such a woman loves you passionately and knows all your faults and weaknesses. If you spurn her, in her fury she may defame your character and your reputation. Or she may invent some terrible accusation and you may not be able to defend yourself and so be ruined.

8) Her husband has often violated the chastity of your women,

* Divorce does not exist among the Hindus, and widows cannot remarry. A 'twice married' woman is one who is living with a man other than her legal husband as his 'wife.'

so your liaison with his wife could be considered as a just revenge.

9) The woman you truly love is under the influence of this married woman, and by entering into relations with the latter you can perhaps acquire the woman of your desire.

10) This woman may be able to find you a rich and beautiful wife, whom you are too poor to approach directly.

These are some of the reasons which allow a man to enter into relations with the wife of another. But it should be understood that such relationships are only countenanced for the above reasons and never for the satisfaction of carnal desire.

It is, however, forbidden to have intercourse under any circumstances with the following women:

A leper;—A lunatic;—A woman expelled from her caste;—A woman who cannot keep a secret;—A woman who publicly expresses her desire for a man;—A woman who is too fair;—A woman who is too dark;—A woman who emits an unpleasant odor;—A woman who is a close relative;—A woman who is a friend;—A woman who devotes her life to religion;—The wife of a relative, a friend, a Sanskrit scholar or the King.

A woman can sometimes be as true a friend as a man, but the choice of true friends should be restricted to:

Those with whom you have played in the summer dust of childhood;—Those who are bound to you by some obligation;—Those who have the same tastes and the same temperament;—Friends of your student days;—Those who know your faults and your secrets; and those whose weaknesses and secrets are known to you;—The child of your nurse;—Those who were raised with you;—The child of a friend of the family.

A true friend, whether man or woman, should possess the following qualities:

He should tell the truth;—He should be constant;—He should help you to attain your objectives;—He should be firm and faithful;—He should not desire your belongings;—Enemies and ill-wishers should be unable to influence him;—He should guard your secrets as his life.

It is not always possible to address a woman personally or to propose a business venture, if the persons concerned are not well known to you. In these cases it is advisable to use the services of an intermediary.

A successful intermediary should possess the following qualities:

Presence;—Audacity;—A keen judgment of character;—Good manners;—A knowledge of the right time and the right place to propose affairs of a different nature;—Loyalty as regards money and women;—A quick intelligence;—Resourcefulness in case of unseen difficulties.

As the *Shastra* says:

> *A man who is both wise and subtle*
> *Assisted by a cunning friend*
> *Who knows the secrets of time and place*
> *When to speak and when be silent*
> *When a woman's heart is open—*
> *May triumph over all the virtues*
> *Of the most chaste and faithful woman.*

PART TWO

SEXUAL INTERCOURSE

*Diverse kinds of sexual union following the classic
Dimensions; the Force of Desire; the Duration of sexual
pleasures and the Different kinds of Love*

The male sex can be divided into three groups, according to the
size of the sexual organs. These groups are known as the Hare, the
Bull and the Horse.

Similarly women are also divided in three categories, in relation to the size and depth of the Yoni—the Doe, the Mare, and the
Elephant.

It therefore follows that there are three perfect forms of union
between persons of corresponding dimensions, and six unequal or
less satisfactory physical combinations, when the dimensions are
unequal.

The following table illustrates this point more graphically.

EQUAL		UNEQUAL	
HARE	DOE	HARE	MARE
		HARE	ELEPHANT
BULL	MARE	BULL	DOE
		BULL	ELEPHANT
HORSE	ELEPHANT	HORSE	MARE
		HORSE	DOE

When a man has intercourse with a woman whose sexual dimensions are inferior to his, his union with a woman of the category just
below his and the next is known as a High Union. While any re-

lationship with a woman from the category the farthest removed from his is known as a Very High Union.

Contrarily, when a woman's sexual dimension exceeds that of her partners it is called a Low Union or a Very Low Union.

In other words, the Horse and the Mare, the Bull and the Doe form High Unions; while the Horse and the Doe form a Very High Union.

With regard to women—the Elephant and the Bull, the Mare and the Hare form a Very Low Union.

There are therefore nine kinds of Union possible in relation to sexual dimensions. Intercourse between people of equal dimensions is best, while the two extremes, the Very Low Unions and the Very High Unions, are worst. Among the other possibilities, the High Unions are more agreeable than unions where the woman possesses the superior organ.

Another factor that conditions sexual behavior is temperament. It is obvious that the need for sexual intercourse and desire varies with each person. For the sake of analysis it is perhaps best to divide people once again, into three groups according to their sexual appetite and passion.

One speaks of a man as having a 'small' sexual appetite, when he is not at ease in the passionate embrace of a woman, when he cannot abandon himself at the moment of consummation, and when his sperm is not abundant.

Those who have a warmer nature can be said to have a 'medium' temperament; while those who are full of carnal desire are known as men of 'intense' passion.

Women can also be classified in the above manner.

The element of time is very important in regard to sexual intercourse. Again it is possible to divide human beings into three categories:

a) Those who reach their climax very quickly;

b) Those who need a certain amount of time;

c) Those who are exceedingly slow.

However, with regard to women, there exists some difference on this last point.

Auddalika says: 'Women do not generally come with the same force as men. Men simply assuage their desire; while women, with their basically puritan temperaments, feel a certain pleasure during the act. But, it is impossible for them to define this pleasure, or to say exactly what it is. The proof lies in the fact that after the orgasm the man voluntarily ceases the coitus, while this is not the case with women.'

Yet, it is well known that women enjoy the sexual act being prolonged, and if a man arrives at his climax too quickly, tney feel angry and frustrated. Some of the ancient Masters interpret this as proof that a woman has as strong an orgasm as a man.

There is also an ancient verse which states:

The Desire, the passion and lubricity of a woman
Are calmed by violent coupling with a man;
And the pleasures of the coitus
Are called by some their satisfaction.

The disciples of Bhabravya, on the other hand, affirm that the 'sperm' of woman is ejected from the beginning to the end of union. This theory is not valid, for sexual passion follows the same laws of motion as a potter's wheel, or an object rolling down a hill. At the beginning the woman is only partially aroused, and she can hardly equal her lover's ardor; but by degrees her passion increases until she loses all consciousness of her body involved in the rhythm and motion of the act, until at last, the momentum ceases, and she feels the need to stop.

The sperm of a man springs like a fountain-jet
When passion is appeased at the end of coitus:
But the life-seed of a woman flows like a continuous stream,
And, when the spring is dry, and the river bed lies empty,
Then passion ceases, and the struggle dies its death.

It has often been asked why, assuming that men and women belong to the same species, and seek similar satisfaction in the sexual act, they have different functions to fulfill.

It is evident that men and women play different rôles. It can even be said that their concept of pleasure is different. In coitus, man is the Aggressive force, woman the Receptive, which is basically the rôle of the male and female in nature itself. This difference in action is directly linked to a difference of concept. The man says of the act of love: 'This woman is united to *me*'; while the woman thinks: 'I am united to this man.'

It is possible to infer from this, that if men and women act in different rôles, the pleasure they feel is also different.

This is not true, because men and women have different personalities, and it is this that causes them to play different rôles, but this does not imply that they do not derive the same degree of pleasure from the act they mutually accomplish.

One can perhaps best compare it to a battle between two rams, who charge from opposite directions and meet with a head-on clash. And if one draws the comparison further, it can be pointed out that the nature of the elements involved is the same. Thus one can conclude that the nature of man and woman engaged in amorous combat is also the same, and as the difference of their acts is merely a difference of natural tradition, it follows that men experience the same pleasure as women.

Having proved that men and women experience the same pleasure in intercourse, it should be borne in mind that there are nine kinds of sexual union with regard to dimension, nine with regard to temperament, and nine with regard to time and speed. Thus the combinations possible are infinite and consequently, to achieve a perfect sexual union, the man must use his judgment in each particular case to overcome any discrepancies that might exist.

For example, it is known that the first time a man and woman make love the man's passion is intense, and he reaches his orgasm very quickly, while a woman is only half aroused. Later, however, it is quite the opposite. The woman's passion grows, and she speeds to her fulfillment while the man's passion successively decreases.

Different Kinds of Love

Scholars who are versed in the humanities define four kinds of love:

1) Love that results from the execution, constant and continued, of a certain act is known as Love acquired through Constant Practice and Habit. For example, the love of sexual intercourse, the love of alcohol, gambling and sports.

2) Love that is felt for things out of the ordinary, and which is entirely based on the imagination or intellect, is called Love as the result of Imagination. For example, the love certain men or women feel for oral intercourse, and the love everyone feels for kisses, caresses, etc.

3) Love that is completely reciprocal and sincere, and when each one sees in the other the complement of himself, is known as Love as the result of Faith.

4) Love as a result of the Perception of Exterior Objects is known to everyone, as the sight of a beautiful woman has moved more poets to verse, and lovers to madness than any other form of love.

What has been exposed in this chapter is sufficient for the experienced man; but for the inexperienced the shastras will explore the subject in greater detail.

26

CHAPTER 2

Embraces and Caresses

The section of the Kama Shastra which deals with sexual intercourse is known as Chatushshashti or sixty-four.

Some ancient writers claim it is so called because it is divided into sixty-four parts.

Others claim that the author of this important part of the Kama Shastra was a certain Panchala and, as the devotees who recite the section of the Rig Veda known as Dashatapa—which contains sixty-four verses—are also known as Panchala, these same authors claim that the name sixty-four was given in honor of the Rig Veda.

On the other hand the disciples of Bhabravya point out that this section of the Kama Shastra encompasses eight subjects: the Caress, the Kiss, the Scratch, the Bite, Sexual Union, the Production of different Erotic Cries, the Woman Assuming the rôle of the Man, and Oral Intercourse. Each of these sections is again divided into eight parts, making sixty-four in all, and it is for this reason that it is called Chatushshashti.

But Vatsyayana disagrees and contests that this portion of the Shastras includes many more subjects than the eight listed above, such as blows, cries, the behavior of the man during intercourse, different methods of sexual intercourse, and many other details, and it is only because of hazard and tradition that this section is known as sixty-four. For example, one often says: "This tree is Saptaparna or the tree of the seven leaves; or this offering of rice is known as 'Panchavarna' or five colors," though the tree does not necessarily possess only seven leaves nor the rice only five colors.

Whatever the reasons may be, the first subject treated in this section known as sixty-four is the Embrace.

The embrace is the bodily contact which reflects the joy of a man and a woman united in love.

The old writings state that there are four kinds of embrace:

1) When a man, feeling the hard bite of desire, touches a woman's body with his own (generally using some pretext or excuse, for this is the most elementary of all bodily contacts), it is known as the *Embrace of Touch.*

2) If, in some secluded room, a woman bends down to pick something up, and in doing so her breasts gently pierce her lover's body and are at once seized by him—it is known as the *Embrace of Penetration.*

These two forms of bodily contact are used only by lovers who are not yet sure of their mutual feelings and intentions.

3) When two lovers slowly walk together down some quiet shaded garden gently rubbing their bodies, one against the other, it is known as the *Embrace of Friction*.

4) But when one presses his body strongly and passionately against that of his lover it is known as the *Embrace of Pressure*.

These last two are used by those who have already succumbed to the arrows of Kama, and who are willing to float together on the stormy sea of desire.

When a man and woman meet with the sole object of entering into the reciprocal pleasures of love, they generally embrace in one of the following ways:

5) When a woman clasps her lover as closely as a serpent twines around a tree, and pulls his head towards her waiting lips, if she then kisses him making a light hissing sound 'soutt soutt' and looks at him long and tenderly—her pupils dilated with desire—this posture is known as the *Clasp of the Serpent*.

6) When a woman places one foot on the foot of her lover, and the other around his thigh, when she puts one arm around his neck and the other around his loins, and softly croons her desire, as if she wished to climb the firm stem of his body and capture a kiss—it is known as the *Tree Climber*.

But these two attitudes of passion are only a prelude to the actual union.

7) When a man and a woman, lying on a bed, embrace each other so closely that their arms and thighs are entwined in a gentle friction, it is called the *Union of the Sesame Seed with the Grain of Rice*.

8) When a man and a woman take each other violently and without fear of pain or harm, as if one wished to penetrate the body of the other, even if the woman is sitting astride his knees or standing against him or lying beneath him, her abandonment is known as the *Union of Milk and Water*.

These last two passionate embraces take place at the actual moment of sexual union. These are the eight different kinds of embraces according to the disciples of Bhabravya.

However, one of the most ancient masters, Suvarnanabha, adds that there are also four basic ways of embracing separate parts of the body.

1) If two lovers press their thighs one against the other, it is the *Caress of Two Thighs*.

2) If a man presses the 'Jaghana'—the part of the body between the navel and the thighs—of the woman closely and mounts her

naked body either to scratch her, or bite her, or hit her, or kiss her, and unties the heavy knot of her hair, it is known as the *Caress of the Jaghana*.

3) When a man rubs his chest against the soft breasts of his partner, it is known as the *Caress of Two Breasts*.

4) When a lover presses his mouth, eyes and forehead against the mouth, eyes and forehead of the other, it is called the *Caress of the Forehead*.

Some writers claim that massage can also be considered as a kind of embrace or caress, since it involves a certain friction and contact between two bodies. But Vatsyayana disagrees with this, as massage is usually performed in quite another mood with another object in mind, and it is of a completely different character and therefore cannot be strictly classified as a caress or an embrace.

Any discussion on the caresses permitted between a man and a woman is both varied and passionate, and any man listening to such a conversation at once feels the cunning knife of desire stab between his loins. Certain strange caresses not mentioned in the Kama Shastra should however be practiced during sexual union if they lead to the heightening of mutual pleasure and to a more intimate knowledge of the desired body. The rules of the Shastra are only applicable when a man retains control of himself and is not drowned in his passion, but once the wheel of Kama starts to turn, there is neither Shastra nor rules, only the numbing ecstasy of motion.

CHAPTER 3

The Kiss

Some people claim that there can be no definite rules nor order laid down for kisses, caresses, pressure or scratches, but that all these things find their place during the prelude to sexual union; while blows and cries usually accompany the act itself. Vatsyayana agrees that these little acts of love should be practiced at any time either separately or altogether, as in love there is no thought of order or time.

The first time one performs the act of love, kisses, scratches, bites and other such caresses should be used with moderation and the whole act of love should not last long. But on following occasions, on the contrary, all moderation should be thrown aside, the act should be prolonged for as long as is possible, and to make the fires of desire burn even more brightly, all manner of caresses, cries and other stimulants to love should be used.

The Kiss should be imprinted on the following parts of the body: the forehead, the eyes, the cheeks, the throat, the chest, the breasts, the lips and the interior of the mouth.

But the natives from the province of Lat also kiss the following parts of the body: the thighs, the arms and the navel. Vatsyayana, however, is of the opinion that though these people use the kiss more widely because of their passionate natures, and embrace these other parts of the body, they conform to the custom and practices of their province, and it is therefore doubtful whether these practices are suitable for people from other lands and backgrounds.

If the woman in question is a young virgin engaged in her first battle with passion, the lover should employ the following three kisses:

The Nominal;—The Palpitating;—The Touch.

1) When a young girl merely brushes her lover's mouth with her own, it is called a Nominal Kiss.

2) When a young maiden, overcoming her shyness, touches her lover's mouth with her own and moves only her lower lip, it is the Palpitating Kiss.

3) When the young girl brushes her lover's lips with her tongue, closes her eyes and places her hands in his, it is known as the Touch Kiss.

However, other writers on the subject describe four other kinds of kisses:

The Direct Kiss;—The Inclined Kiss;—The Turning Kiss;—The Pressed Kiss.

1) When the lips of two lovers come directly into contact, it is called a Direct Kiss.

2) When the heads of the lovers are turned, one up, one down, towards the other, this kiss on the mouth is the Inclined Kiss.

3) When the lover takes his mistress' chin in his hand and turns her face towards him and then kisses her on the mouth, moving her head slightly from side to side, this is the Turning Kiss.

There is also a fifth kind of kiss that is known as the 'Kiss of Great Pressure.' This is practiced in the following way: the lover clasps the lower lip in his fingers and brushes it with his tongue, then he seizes it with his lips and presses it with great force.

Before the act one may amuse oneself by playing a little game of who can seize the other's lips first. If the woman loses she must sulk, push her lover away, turn her back on him and try to quarrel with him saying, 'I want a revenge.' If she loses a second time, she must pretend to be twice as upset, and then when her lover is preoccupied or asleep she must seize his lower lip between her teeth so that he cannot pull it way. Then she can burst out laughing, make a great deal of noise, make fun of him, dance around him and, raising her eyebrows and rolling her eyes roguishly, say whatever comes into her head. These are the games which may be played with kisses. Of course the same kind of game may also be played with scratches, bites, caresses and palpation. However, it should be noted that these little games are only practiced by men and women of passionate temperament.

When a man kisses the upper lip of a woman and she returns his caress by embracing his lower lip, it is known as the Kiss of the Upper Lip.

When one of the two partners seizes the lips of the other between his own, this is known as the Close Kiss. But this kiss can only be practiced by a man without moustaches. And if, during this kiss, one of the lovers touches the teeth, tongue or palate of the other with his tongue, it is known as the Combat of Tongues. In the same way, one can also practice this kiss by pressing the teeth against the teeth of the loved one.

Kisses can generally be divided into four categories: Moderated, Contracted, Pressed and Gentle, according to the part of the body on which they are imprinted, because different kinds of kisses are appropriate to different parts of the body.

When a woman gazes longingly at her lover while he is asleep and kisses him to show her love and desire, this is known as the Kiss which Arouses.

When a woman kisses her lover while he is working or scolding her, or when he is preoccupied, so as to distract him and to divert his attention to her, it is known as the Kiss that Distracts.

When a lover comes home late and kisses his sleeping mistress so as to gently waken her, it is known as the Kiss of Awakening. In the same way, a woman can pretend to sleep when she hears her lover enter the room, so that he can make his intentions clear to her, and she will win his respect by not anticipating his desire or being too forward.

When one kisses the image of the loved one reflected in a mirror, on still waters or on a wall, it is called the Kiss of Intention.

If one kisses a child, a painting or an image in the presence of the loved person, this is known as the Kiss that is Transferred.

If a man meets his mistress at the theater or during a gathering of friends of the same caste, and he kisses her hand if she is standing, or her toe if she is seated, it is known as a Demonstrative Kiss. The same is true if a woman lays her head on her lover's thigh while she is massaging his body, or if during the massage she embraces his thigh or his big toe.

> *No matter what one lover does,*
> *The other must return the favor.*
> *If the woman kisses the man*
> *The man must return her kiss,*
> *If she bites or if she beats him,*
> *With twice the force he must beat her in return.*

CHAPTER 4

Scratches and Marks made with the Fingers

The subtle and hard pressure of the fingers or the nails pressed deep into the body are the sure signs of mounting passion. These painful caresses should be performed during the first visit; at parting for a voyage; at the moment of return from a long absence; at the moment of reconciliation with an angry lover; or when a woman is drunk.

But these wild caresses are only practiced by lovers whose temperaments are intense and passionate. And those who delight in these signs of love also take pleasure in bites inflicted during the act of love.

There are eight different kinds of pressure and they are named after the form and shape of the marks they make on the skin:

1) Sonorous;—2) Half Moon;—3) Circle;—4) Line;—5) The Tiger's Claw;—6) The Peacock's Claw;—7) The Leap of the Hare;—8) The Leaf of the Blue Lotus.

The parts of the body on which these caresses should be perpetrated are: the armpit, the throat, the breast, the lips, the jaghana or center of the body and the thighs. But Suvarnanabha is of the opinion that if a man is intensely passionate, he should not worry where he inflicts the signs of his love.

The qualities which distinguish good nails are that they should be brilliant, clean, well set, whole, convex, soft and polished. There are three categories of nails—short, medium and long.

Long, oval nails which lend an air of grace to the hand and which attract the desire of women are typical of the people of Bengal.

Short nails, which may be used in diverse ways to procure pleasure, are possessed by the people of the South.

Medium-sized nails which possess all the properties of the other two are found among the natives of Maharashtra.

1) When a person presses the lips, the breast, the lower lip or the jaghana of his lover so gently that no mark remains and the hair of the body rises in response to the caress and the fingers make a soft clicking sound, this is known as the Sonorous pressure of the nails.

This gentle caress is usually used on a young and inexperienced maiden when her lover massages her body, scratches her head or wishes to arouse her.

2) The curved mark left by a nail on the throat or the breasts is known as the Half Moon.

3) When the Half Moons are imprinted one against the other it is known as the Circle. This mark is usually made around the navel, in the hollows of the buttocks and on the joints of the thighs.

4) A mark in the form of a little line that one can make on any part of the body is called the Line.

5) The same line if it is slightly curved and imprinted on the chest is called the Tiger's Claw.

6) When one traces five curved lines with the fingers of one hand on the chest it is called the Peacock's Claw. This mark on the body is mainly inflicted for the sake of prestige, for it calls for a great deal of finesse to execute this caress artistically and accurately.

7) When marks of the five nails are made one after the other around the nipples, this is known as the Leap of the Hare.

8) A mark on the chest or on the buttock in the shape of a Leaf of the Blue Lotus is known by that name.

When a person about to leave for a long journey inflicts a mark on his beloved's thigh or chest, it is known as the Mark of Remembrance. On such occasions it is usually customary to imprint three or four little lines with the fingers.

These, however, are not the only marks that can be made with the nails. For, as the ancient authors so wisely observe, an experienced man well versed in the diverse aspects of the science of love will invent innumerable, varied and artistic signs to impose on his mistress' body as symbols of his love. And as these scars depend on the depth and force of a man's passion, it is impossible to enumerate the many varieties that exist or are possible. For, says Vatsyayana, if variety is desirable in love, then love must be aroused by a variety of means. This is also one of the reasons why courtesans are so sought after, for they, of all women, know the multiple varied and subtle caresses involved in the act of passion. The variety which one seeks in all arts and amusements, even in archery or other such sports, how much more important is it in the art of love.

Lovers should not, however, leave these traces of their affection on the bodies of married women, though they may inflict particular signs on their secret and private parts to increase their love and desire.

> *A woman who finds the marks of love*
> *On the innermost and secret parts of her being*
> *Though these marks be faded and effaced*
> *Finds her love born anew with memory.*
> *If nails do not mark the steps that love has trodden*
> *Then desire dies, as when, after long absence*
> *The body grows cold as the memory of passion fades.*

When a stranger sees the marks of love on a young woman's breast he is filled with desire and respect for her. In the same way, a man who bears the scars of slender nails on the secret parts of his body arouses the desire of the most steadfast woman. In short, there are few things that arouse love so successfully as the sight of the scars left by former nights of passion.

CHAPTER 5

Loves bites and techniques to be used
on women from different lands

All the parts of the body that can be kissed can also be bitten except the upper lip, the interior of the mouth and the eyes.

Good teeth are equal in length, brilliant in color, beautiful to see, of good proportions, whole, intact and sharp at the extremities.

Wide, soft, uneven, badly spaced and discolored teeth are ugly and repulse a lover.

The different kinds of love bites are known as:

The Hidden Bite;—The Swollen Bite;—The Point·—The Line

of Points;—The Coral and the Jewel;—The Line of Jewels;—The Broken Cloud;—The Bite of the Wild Boar.

1) The Hidden Bite betrays itself only by a slight redness of the skin.

2) The Swollen Bite is a bite in which a portion of the skin swells into a lump.

3) The Point is where a small portion of the skin is bitten only by two teeth.

4) When small parts of the skin are marked by all the teeth, it is called a Line of Points.

5) The Coral and the Jewel is the bite which is inflicted by the lips and the teeth together. The lips are the coral and the teeth the jewels.

6) When a bite is imprinted with all the teeth, it is known as a Line of Jewels.

7) A bite in the form of an uneven circle—the unevenness being due to the shape and form of the teeth—is called the Broken Cloud.

8) The bite which is formed by large teeth marks interspaced with patches of reddened skin is called the Bite of the Wild Boar.

This last bite is always imprinted on the breasts and is a typical indication of a very passionate and fierce lover.

The Hidden Bite, the Swollen Bite and the Point are usually imprinted on the lower lip; while the Coral and the Jewel are best placed on the cheek. Kisses, scars left by the nails, and bites are the ornaments of the left cheek, and when one refers to the cheek in matters of love it is always the left cheek which is implied.

The Line of Points and the Line of Jewels must both be imprinted on the neck, armpit and the joints of the thighs, but the former may also be inflicted on the forehead and the thighs.

If one marks with one's nails or bites the following objects, an ornament for the hair, an earring, a bouquet of flowers, a betel or tamal leaf which are worn by the beloved or belong to her, these marks symbolize the desire of the lover to enjoy his mistress.

Techniques to be used on women from other lands.

In matters of love a man must learn to please and satisfy women from all parts of the land.

The women from the region between the Ganges and the Jumna are noble and are not accustomed to disagreeable practices. They are horrified by such signs of passion as bites and scratches.

Women from the province of Balhika give themselves to the men who beat them.

The women of Avantika love vulgar pleasures and are generally of an immoral nature.

The women of Maharashtra love to practice the sixty-four arts; they murmur crude and lascivious words during the act of love and delight in being abused and addressed lasciviously. They are capable of having repeated orgasms and are indefatigable lovers.

The women of Pataliputra have the same temperament as the women of Maharashtra but they are secretive and only reveal their desires in private.

The women from the lands of the Dravidians are very placid. No matter how much a man may caress their yoni or how hard he may copulate they remain dry and have a very slow and brief orgasm.

The women of Vanavasi are only moderately passionate. They love all kinds of amusements and games, but they cover their bodies during intercourse and reprimand their lovers if they murmur low, lascivious or vulgar words during the act.

The women of Avanti hate kisses, caresses or love bites, but they delight in many varied methods of intercourse.

The women of Malva like to be embraced and kissed, but without violence and they give themselves to those who beat them.

The women of Abhira between the Indus and the five rivers are passionately fond of oral intercourse.

The women of Aparatika are very passionate and they very slowly make the sound 'Sitt.'

The women of Stri Rajya and of Koshola are passionate and impetuous. They have many repeated orgasms and they love to drug themselves to facilitate the orgasm.

The women of Andhra have soft and tender bodies. They love to be amused and are given to all kinds of sensual pleasures.

The women of Canada have soft hearts and speak quietly and gently.

According to Suvarnanabha, the individual tastes of a person are of much greater importance than the customs or traditions of the country. So that in matters of love one should be guided by the personal tastes of the woman and please her desires, even if her tastes may be different from most of the other women in her province. Often, the ways, codes, traditions, fashions and customs of one country are completely assimilated by another province, and in such cases these foreign customs practised by the inhabitants must be considered as original and indigenous to the country.

The caresses, bites and scratches mentioned above should be practiced to arouse passion; but they should only be used as amusements or diversions.

> *When a man bites his mistress in the violence of love*
> *She should return his gesture with twice the force;*
> *Thus for a point she should tender a line of points*
> *And for a line of points—a broken cloud—*
> *And if breathless with passion she should accuse her lover*
> *And provoke a lovers' quarrel, seize him by the hair,*
> *Bend his head and fiercely embrace his lower lip,*
> *Then closing her eyes she should bite him all over*
>   *[his body*
> *As an animal in the fury of passion does its mate.*
> *Even in the daytime when her lover shows her the*
> *She inflicted on him in love's battle,*   *[scars*
> *She should smile, turn her head, then angrily show*
> *The wounds his love has left on her.*
> *Thus, if men and women act in mutual accord,*
> *Their passion and desire for each other*
> *Will not diminish even after a hundred years of love.*

CHAPTER 6

The Postures and Attitudes during Intercourse

In a High Union the Mrigi or doe woman must lie in such a way that her yoni is distended and enlarged; while, during a Low Union, the Elephant woman should place herself in a position that will contract her huge cavity. But in an equal union they should lie in a natural position. This also holds true for the Vadawa or Mare. In a Low Union women should make use of drugs to sharpen their desire and hasten their orgasm.

The three best positions for a Mrigi or doe to adopt during intercourse are:

The large open position;—The wide open position;—The position of the wife of Indra.

The large open position is when the Mrigi lowers her head and raises the jaghana. The man should use some ointment to make penetration painless and easy.

2) When she raises her thighs and spreads her legs wide, it is known as the Wide Open position.

3) The position of Indrani is more complicated. The Mrigi must pull her knees up on to her chest, with her legs flattened against the thighs. This position can only be learned by repeated practice and it can also be used if engaged in a Very High Union.

The Close position is used in Low Union and in Very Low Union, concurrently with the Squeezed position, the Gentle position and the position of the Mare.

1) When the legs of the man and the woman are stretched out one against the other, this is known as the Closed position. There are two sorts of closed positions: on the side and on the back. When a man engages in closed intercourse on his side, he must always lie on his left side and place the woman on her right side. This rule is applicable to women from all lands.

2) When intercourse has begun in the Closed position and the woman presses her lover's thighs between her thighs, this is called the Squeezed position.

3) When a woman places one of her thighs across the thighs of her seducer, this is known as the Entwined position.

4) And finally when a woman contracts the muscles of her yoni and holds the lingam prisoner within her, it is known as the position of the Mare. This technique can only be learned by practice, and the sweet, fresh women of Andhra are well known for their ability to use this delicious practice.

These are the different methods or positions of sexual intercourse as listed by Bhabravya. However, Suvarnanabha includes many more:

When a woman raises her two thighs straight up, it is known as the Raised position.

When her two legs are placed on the shoulders of her lover, Suvarnanabha refers to it as the Wide Open position.

When her legs are contracted and bent back by her lover against her chest it is known as the Pressed position.

When one leg is stretched straight out and the other is contracted against the chest, it is known as the Half-pressed position.

When a woman places one foot on her lover's shoulder and stretches the other horizontally on the bed, then alters the position by changing the position of the legs, it is known as the Bamboo Cleft.

If one leg is placed on the lover's head while the other is stretched out horizontally, it is called the Nail. But this position can only be practiced by experienced and passionate lovers.

When the two legs of the woman are contracted and placed on her stomach, it is known as the position of the Crab.

If the thighs are raised and placed one on top of the other, it is known as the Packet.

When the legs are folded one on top of the other and then raised, it is known as the position of the Lotus.

When a man revolves his hips round and round during intercourse, while the woman twines her feet around his loins, it is known as the Revolving position.

Suvarnanabha claims that all complicated and difficult positions and acts, whether performed sitting, standing or lying, should first be tried in water, as this facilitates access and renders it possible to master these difficult though pleasurable techniques. But Vatsyayana disagrees with him, and states that intercourse in water is forbidden by the scriptures.

When a man and woman press their bodies one against the other or if they lean against a pillar or a wall and indulge in intercourse standing upright, it is known as the Leaning position.

When a man leans against the wall and the woman sits on his hands while he supports her buttocks, and pressing her thighs around his waist she engages in the rhythmic movement of union with her feet pressed against the wall, it is known as the Suspended position.

When the woman goes down on all fours like an animal and her lover mounts her as if he were a bull or a stallion, it is known as the position of the Cow. In these circumstances it is usual to perform all the auxiliary actions of love on the back instead of on the breasts.

One can also vary this last form of union by adopting the position of the Dog, the union of the Goat, the Doe, the violent assault of the Ass, the union of the Cat, the bound of the Tiger, the pressure of the Elephant, the rubbing movements of the Wild Boar, and the charge of the Stallion. The man should, in these cases, imitate the actions and sounds of the different animals.

When a man possesses two women at the same time, it is known as Uniter Intercourse.

When a man enjoys many women at the same time, it is known as the Union of the Bull with the Cows.

This last form of intercourse can also be varied, such as the Union of the Elephant with his Mates, which should always be performed in water; while in the Union of the Goat with a Troop of Females or the Union of the Stag and a Herd of Does, the man should imitate the action of these animals and mount his women one after the other.

In the province of Gramaneri, many young men enjoy the same woman—who may be married to one of them—either all together at the same time, or one after the other. Thus one holds her and excites her with caresses, another penetrates her yoni, a third her mouth, while a fourth does his act on her stomach, and in this way they change places and enjoy her in turn.

The same thing often takes place when several men find themselves visiting the same courtesan. And the women of the King's Harem often enjoy a man together if by chance they manage to smuggle him past the eunuchs and the palace guards.

The people of the southern lands often enjoy penetrating the anus, but this is known as Inferior Intercourse.

> An ingenious and sensual lover
> Should mutiply the act of love by a million;
> Imitate the ways and cries of birds and beasts,
> For imagination, lightly bound by custom and tradition,
> Which varies the delights of love each time,
> Opens a woman's heart and engenders there
> Love, respect, friendship and submission.

CHAPTER 7

The various ways to hit a woman and the accompanying sounds

Sexual intercourse can be compared to a lovers' quarrel, because of the little annoyances so easily caused by love and the tendency on the part of two passionate individuals to change swiftly from love to anger. In the intensity of passion one often hits the lover on the body, and the parts of the body where these blows of love should be dealt are:

The shoulders;—The head;—The space between the breasts;—The back;—The jaghana;—The sides.

There are also four ways of hitting the loved one:

With the back of the hand;—With the fingers slightly contracted; —With the fist;—With the palm of the hand.

These blows are painful and the person hit often emits a cry of pain. There are eight sounds of pleasurable anguish which correspond to the different kinds of blows. These are the sounds:

Hinn;—A tonal sound;—A cooing sound;—A crying sound;— Phoutt;—Phatt;—Soutt;—Platt.

Aside from these sounds the victim of love's pleasure sometimes cries out words such as 'Mother,' which expresses her desires to be free, her satisfaction, a wish that the punishment should cease, sometimes praise of her lover's power, or pain. To these words can be added the sounds of the dove, the cuckoo, the green pigeon, the parakeet, the bee, the sparrow, the flamingo, the duck and the partridge.

The man should hit the woman with his closed fist when she sits on his knees. She should return his blows with force and scold him as if she were angry with him, accompanied by weeping and cooing sounds. When intercourse begins the man gently hits the space between the breasts with the back of the hand, slowly at first, and then harder and faster in rhythm with the mounting excitement of intercourse. At this moment, one should emit the panting sound *Hinn* and others like it according to the customs and language of the country.

When a man makes the sound *Phatt* and hits the woman on the head with his fingers slightly contracted, this is known as *Prasritaka,* which means 'to hit with contracted fingers.' In this case the appropriate sounds to accompany the action are the sounds *Phatt* and *Phoutt* made in the interior of the mouth, and at the end of intercourse certain sighing and weeping noises. The sound *Phatt* is an imitation of the sound made by breaking a bamboo. The sound *Phoutt* resembles the sound of an object falling in water. Every time the lover kisses or caresses his mistress, she should express her appreciation and satisfaction by emitting a soft whistling sound.

If the woman is not used to being hit during intercourse she should murmur soft words of pain and suffering, such as 'Mother' and 'Oh! Mother,' alternated with sighing, weeping and harsh sounds. Just before the lover reaches his climax, he should press the breasts, jaghana and waist of the woman very hard with the palms of his hands, increasing the pressure until he reaches his pleasure, and the woman should reply to his urgency by murmuring sounds like those made by a partridge or goose.

To the four ways of hitting the beloved during sexual intercourse may be added the use of a stamp on the breast, a pair of scissors on the head, sharp instruments on the cheeks and pincers on the 'breasts and sides, which all in all add up to eight different kinds of blows. But these last four methods, which employ the use of instruments, are particular to people from the south, and one can see the scars left by these objects on the breasts and bodies of the women of these lands. These ways of lovemaking are particular to certain localities, but Vatsyayana is of the opinion that these methods are dangerous, painful, and barbarous, and should not be imitated.

In general, special methods of intercourse which are particular to one group of people should not be blindly adopted by anyone not used to such practices. But if anyone is attracted by such methods, he should examine the problem carefully from all sides and then use these techniques in moderation, taking care not to offend the customs and traditions prevalent in his own region. History records some of the dangers of these practices:

The King of the Panchalas killed the beautiful courtesan, Madhavasena, by hitting her with an iron stamp during the excitement of intercourse.

Shatakarni Shatavahana, King of the Kuntalas, stabbed his famous Queen Malayavati to death using a pair of scissors during intercourse.

Naradeva, whose hand was slightly paralyzed, blinded a young dancer when a sharp instrument slipped out of control during the passionate struggle of intercourse.

In regard to these methods of love, it is impossible to establish a method or definite rules. Once two people start on the road of intercourse, passion and passion alone guides their movements and acts.

Passionate gestures, acts or movements which are born of sexual desire and excitement cannot be defined. They are as ephemeral as dreams. A horse which has attained the fifth degree of speed continues his mad gallop without regard for the holes, ditches, or trees that may lie along his mad course. Thus two lovers in the heat and sweat of excitement are blinded by mutual passion and pursue their mad course of pleasure with fury and without regard for the excesses they may commit during the act. It is for this reason that a man who is familiar with the science of love and who knows the depth of his passion and his own strength, as well as the forces, affection and temperament of his partner, takes these factors into consideration and chooses the methods of his union accordingly. The different methods of sexual union are not suitable to all times and all places, and the wise man must use his judgment and select those that are suited to his needs and which also conform to the customs and usages of his country and society.

Force and impetuosity are characteristic of the Male,
While tenderness, sensitivity and a desire to avoid
Unpleasantness are distinctive of the Female.
The blind excitement of passion and personal idiosyncrasy
Lead to contradictory action at times
But the lovers' desire for Union
Always ends by imposing its natural laws
On both man and woman alike.

CHAPTER 8

Women who play the rôle of the Man

When the woman sees that her lover is exhausted by prolonged intercourse, even before he has reached his climax, she must with his consent gently push him onto his back and come to his help by assuming his rôle. She may also undertake to adopt the position normally held by the man in intercourse just to satisfy his curiosity or because she feels a need for variety.

There are two ways of performing this function. Either the woman should turn around and mount her lover without interrupting the intercourse between them, or she should adopt the rôle of the man from the very beginning.

With her hair strewn with flowers lying loose on her back, smiling and breathless she should gently rub her breasts against his chest and frequently bending her head she should return his blows, love bites, kisses and seductive words of love, saying: 'You pushed me down and ground the very center of my being; now it is my turn to lay you on your back and to grind you.'

Then she should pretend to be suddenly overcome by modesty and refuse to continue to play her rôle. Thus alternately daring and timid, she should act the rôle of the male.

The rôle or the work of man consists in doing everything that can give pleasure to a woman.

For instance, when a woman is lying on the bed engaged in the teasing conversation of love, the man should gently untie her robe, and if she begins to protest and to scold him, he should silence her protests with kisses. As soon as his lingam is in erection, he should let his hands subtly wander over her body and delicately press and palpitate certain ultra-sensitive parts. If the woman is shy and it is the first time that they are engaged in carnal intercourse, the lover should slip his hands between her thighs and force her to part her limbs. Or if it is a very young girl, he should first seize her breasts—which she will undoubtedly try to protect from his onslaught by covering them with her hands—and then he should slip his arms under her armpits and clasp her around the neck. If, on the other hand, his mistress is an experienced woman, he should caress her in the manner which he knows will please her most and which is also appropriate to the circumstances. Thereafter, he should entwine his hand in her hair, raise her chin and cover her face with kisses. If his mistress is a young maiden, she will be overcome and close her eyes, but whatever the circumstances, the expression on his mistress' face is the best indication of what he must do to make the union satisfying to her.

Here Suvarnanabha interposes to advise that though a man may be doing everything that he considers desirable to his mistress, he must always take great care to caress and kiss the parts of her body she may happen to glance at in her agitation.

If a woman is pleased and satisfied and reaches her climax at the same time as her lover, her body relaxes, she closes her eyes, forgets all modesty, and shows an increasing desire to unite the two organs as closely as possible.

On the other hand, if she is unsatisfied, she wrings her hands, does not allow her lover to rise, seems defeated, bites and hits him, urging him to continue long after he has reached his climax. In such a case, the man should rub her yoni—as the elephant caresses with his trunk—until her agitation calms down, then he should once again introduce his lingam into her and begin over again.

The following are the normal actions of a man:

The advance forward;—To rub or batter;—To pierce;—To beat; —To press;—To give a blow;—The attack of the wild boar;—The attack of the bull;—Chasing the sparrow.

1) When the organs approach each other simply and directly, is it is called the Advance Forward.

2) When he holds his lingam in his hand and turns it round within the yoni, it is called Rubbing.

3) If the yoni is lying low and the lingam in penetration comes into contact with the upper part of the yoni, it is known as Piercing.

4) When the same thing occurs, only it is the lower part of the yoni that comes into contact with the lingam, it is called Beating.

5) When the yoni is held against the lingam for a long time, it is known as Pressing.

6) When the lingam is withdrawn and then enters the yoni with great force, it is commonly said to Deal a Blow.

7) When the lingam rubs only one side of the yoni, it is the Attack of the Wild Boar.

8) When both sides of the yoni are hit by the lingam, it is the attack of the Bull.

9) When the lingam is in the yoni and the man thrusts with his loins engaging in a rapid in-and-out action without once removing his organ, it is known as Chasing the Sparrow and is the last act of Sexual union.

When the woman plays the part of a man, she must in addition to the nine actions listed above perform:

The pair of pincers;—The top;—The swing.

1) When the woman introduces the lingam within her, contracts her muscles to suck it deeper within her, squeezes it and holds it within her for a long time, it is known as the Pair of Pincers.

2) The Top is when a woman turns round and round on the stem of the lingam. This can only be learned with practice.

3) When the man raises the middle part of his body and the woman turns the middle part of her own body round and round, it is known as the Swing.

If the woman is tired, she must rest her forehead against her lover's cheek and lie still without interrupting the contact of the two organs. Then when she is rested the man should turn her around and once again assume the active rôle.

The face of a woman should be her mirror to pleasure
The man should read there her desire and will,
And reading, understanding how he must enjoy her.
No matter how reserved a woman may be,
No matter in what secret depths she hides her feelings,
If once she mounts on her lover's loins
She betrays all her love and all her passion
But the rôle of man is strictly forbidden
To women immured in menstruation,
To those who rise from the couch of childbirth
And to women who are fat and large as the elephant.

CHAPTER 9

Auparishtaka or Oral Intercourse

There exist two kinds of eunuchs or hermaphrodites; those who choose the rôle of men, and those who choose to disguise themselves as women.

The Eunuchs who dress as women imitate the fair sex in every way, in costume, speech, manners, kindness, timidity, gentleness and modesty. And the supreme consecration of love which women receive in the soft depths of the yoni, these eunuchs welcome in their mouths. This is called *Auparishtaka.*

These 'female' eunuchs derive a sensual pleasure from oral intercourse, and at the same time it provides a lucrative means of earning a living, and they lead the lives of courtesans.

The eunuchs who adopt the costumes and character of men keep their sexual practices secret, but when they choose a profession they usually hire themselves out as masseurs. Using the massage as a pretext, these eunuchs subtly caress the thighs of their client, and then gradually move their strong trained fingers over the adjacent areas of his body. If he finds the lingam of his client in erection, he gently rubs and presses it with his hands. He makes his intentions quite clear, and if there is no response from the client, the eunuch accepts this silence as acquiescence and introduces the member to his mouth. If, on the contrary, the client becomes aroused and excited by these caresses and orders the eunuch to continue, the masseur refuses and will only finally consent to do so after he has been begged and bribed.

The eunuch then proceeds to introduce his client to the pleasures of the eight different stages of oral intercourse. After each stage he stops and pretends to refuse to continue, but this abrupt and temporary withdrawal only serves to excite his client the more, and he begs the masseur to continue and pays him royally each time for his pains.

The first stage is known as Nominal Union. The eunuch takes his client's organ in his hand and caresses the tip lightly with his lips.

He then clasps the head of the lingam in his hand, with his fingers as tightly closed as the bud of a flower, and roughly kisses and bites the stem of the organ.

If his client begs him to continue, the eunuch seizes the lingam, thrusts it in his mouth and closes his lips tightly, then he pulls

46

with his lips as if he wished to entice the organ away from the body. This is known as Exterior Pressure.

Encouraged by his client's response, the eunuch inserts the lingam more deeply in his mouth, presses it and then suddenly withdraws it. This is called Interior Pressure.

If the eunuch holds the organ in his hand and gently bites it, it is called the Kiss.

On the other hand, if he caresses the lingam with his tongue, especially the extremity, it is known as Polishing.

The culmination of *Auparishtaka* is to be found in the last two stages. The eunuch introduces half the organ into his mouth and caresses it with his tongue and sucks with great force. This is called Eating the Mango.

The climax comes when the eunuch pushes the entire organ into his mouth and presses on it with great force right up to the root, as if he wished to swallow the lingam whole. This is known as Absorption.

The oral union is accompanied by the usual loveplay.

Auparishtaka is not only practiced by the eunuchs. Many dissolute women, prostitutes, and unmarried servant girls (who also work as masseuses) are willing partners to this form of intercourse.

The Acharyas (ancient and venerable authors) claim that this form of intercourse is more suitable for dogs than for men. *Auparishtaka* is forbidden by the Holy Scriptures, which state that it ultimately does a man great harm to constantly insert his lingam into the mouths of eunuchs and prostitutes. Vatsyayana, however, disagrees with the Acharyas and claims that this form of intercourse is only forbidden to married women who are bound by the laws of the Holy Scriptures. He believes that in matters of love, one should be guided by the traditions and practices of the country, but above all by one's own inclinations.

Auparishtaka is not only limited to men. Certain women, especially when they are in love and have not free access to men, caress each other's yonis with their tongues. It ls also known that many men please women with this form of intercourse, as one can apply to the yoni all the varied and diverse forms of kisses that one applies to the mouth. When a man and a woman lie with the head of the one near the feet of the other and indulge in *Auparishtaka*, this is known as the Attitude of the Crow.

Some courtesans are so obsessed by this form of physical pleasure that they abandon rich, honest, and intelligent lovers for base and poor men, such as slaves or elephant boys who will indulge them.

Auparishtaka should never be practiced by a Brahmin scholar, a Minister in charge of Affairs of State, or by a man of good reputation, for though the act is permitted by the Shastras, it should only be used under special and very particular circumstances.

Thus, for example, the taste and health-giving qualities and digestibility of dog's meat is often cited in medical books, but this does not necessarily incline the wise man to eat this meat.

On the other hand, there are times, places and occasions when one must resort to such acts.

A wise man should always first carefully consider the time, place and the act he is about to perform, and if he finds all these factors in harmony and after examination decides that the act will not debase his nature, he may indulge himself in accordance with the circumstances.

But since all such acts are privately performed, and the nature of man being as inconsistent as it is, how can one ever know what a man indulges in behind the locked doors of his chamber?

CHAPTER 10

How to begin and how to end sexual union;
different kinds of union and lovers' quarrels

The citizen surrounded by his friends and servants shall invite the woman he desires—bathed and beautifully dressed—into the perfumed room decorated with flowers that he reserves for such pleasures. Once amongst his friends, he must offer her refreshments and invite her to drink deeply and freely of the heady wines he serves on such occasions. He should make her sit on his left side, and swiftly run his hand over her hair and touch the knot of her robe, and gently encircle her body with his right arm. They should then converse pleasantly on different subjects—and they can exchange secret and private references to things known to both of them but which would be indelicate to discuss publicly in society. They may sing together—with or without gestures— play musical instruments, discuss the arts and incite each other to drink more and more of the cooling and intoxicating wine. And finally, when the woman can no longer hide her breathless need and desire for him, he must gently dismiss his guests, giving each a small present such as flowers, perfumes, or 'pan'; and when they are at last alone, the two of them, they should proceed to their mutual satisfaction along the paths described in the preceding chapters. This is the beginning of sexual intercourse.

At the end, the lovers must part and modestly, without looking at each other, go separately to their toilet. Afterwards, they should sit together and enjoy their feeling of well-being. They should share a 'pan' and the citizen should anoint with some pure extract of sandalwood or other such perfume the body of his beloved. He should put his left arm around her and make her drink water out of a cup which he holds in his right hand. They should eat delicately flavored sweetmeats and drink cool and refreshing juices, soup, gruel, meat extract, sherbets, mango juice or lime juice mixed with some essence that is popular in the land and is known to be sweet, agreeable and pure. The lovers can also sit on the terrace of the mansion and converse softly together in the clear bright moonlight.

With his mistress lying on his knees, her face turned towards the moon, the citizen should show her the different planets, the morning star, the North star, the seven Rishis and the Great Bear. This is the ideal end to sexual intercourse.

Many kinds of union are possible between a man and a woman. There are the:

Union of love;—Union of subsequent love;—Union of artificial affection;—Union of transferred love;—Union similar to the mating of eunuchs;—The disappointing Union;—The Union of spontaneous love.

1) When a man and a woman have loved each other for a long time and find themselves at last united after many difficulties, or when one of the two returns from a voyage, or when they are reconciled after a quarrel, it is known as a Union of Love. This union can be practiced in any way which pleases the lovers and for any length of time.

2) When two people whose love is still in its infancy or in its early stages come together, their union is known as the Union of Subsequent Love.

3) When a man engages in carnal intercourse only after exciting himself by all the methods and means known in the sixty-four arts, or when a man and a woman perform the sexual act though each loves another, it is known as the Union of Artificial Love. Under these circumstances one must employ all the arts and subtleties indicated in the Kama Shastra.

4) If during intercourse with one woman, the man never ceases

49

to think of another and imagines in the darkness that it is she who lies beneath him, it is known as the *Union of Transferred Love*.

5) Intercourse between a man and a water-carrier or a woman of an inferior caste, and which lasts only until his desire has been satiated, is known as the *Union Similar to the Mating of Eunuchs*. If a man has commerce with such women, he should desist from touching, kissing, caressing or in any way fostering a closer intimacy with his partner.

6) Intercourse between a courtesan and a peasant, or between a town-dweller and village woman, or women, coming from the suburbs, is called a Disappointing Union.

7) Union between two people who love each other and who give themselves wholeheartedly and with imagination to the enjoyment of their bodies is known as Spontaneous Union.

Lovers' quarrels

A woman who loves a man passionately can not bear to hear him utter the name of her rival, nor to have any conversation which touches on her, nor to be inadvertently addressed by another woman's name. If such incidents should occur a quarrel arises between the lovers. The woman cries, works herself into a rage, tears her hair, beats her lover, falls from the bed, throws her garlands—and any other object that may unluckily come her way—around the room and falls sobbing to the ground.

The lover should try and calm her fury with conciliating words, and, lifting her carefully, he should carry her back to the bed. But she will not reply to his questions, and holding fast his head she will pull his hair and beat him, once, twice, three times on the arm, the head, the chest, and the back and walk towards the door of the room as if she were about to leave. According to Dattaka, she should sit near the door and weep; but she should not leave for fear of putting herself in the wrong. After some time, when she feels that her lover is truly repentant and has done everything to try and appease her, she should forgive him, kiss him tearfully, skilfully reproaching him, but at the same time she should make him aware of her desire for immediate intercourse.

If the woman is in her own house when she quarrels with her lover, she should make a terrible scene and then leave the house. After some time she should send the Vita, the Vidushaka or the Pithamarda to him to appease him, and then return to the house with them and spend the night with him.

A man who follows the principles of love as indicated by Bhabravya obtains his aims and assures the satisfaction and pleasure of even the finest and most noble women.

Even though a man may be able to discourse brilliantly on many subjects, if he does not know the sixty-four sections and their subtle divisions he will gain but little respect in learned circles.

On the other hand, a man who has very little other knowledge but who is well versed in the sixty-four arts will hold a prominent place in the society of both men and women.

How can one not respect the sixty-four divisions knowing that they are revered by artists, sages and courtesans alike? It is because the sixty-four parts are so respected and because of the charm they possess and the merit they add to the natural attractions of a woman that the Acharyas call them 'The sixty-four arts dear to the female sex.'

A man well versed in these arts is loved by his own wife, by the wives of others and by all the courtesans of the land.

PART THREE

ACQUISITION OF A WIFE

CHAPTER 1

Observations on Betrothal and Marriage

When a young virgin marries according to the rites prescribed by the Holy Scriptures, the results of this union are the acquisition of Dharma and Artha; the assurance of legal posterity, a widening of the circle of acquaintances and a pure and uncomplicated love, undisturbed by the dark clouds of sin or passion.

The perfect wife should be a young girl of good family, whose parents are alive and who is at least three years younger than her husband. She should, if possible, come from a rich and highly respectable family who possess many influential and wealthy friends and relatives. Moreover, the maiden herself should be beautiful and healthy and possess the necessary birthmarks of 'good fortune' on her body. Her fingers, teeth, ears, eyes and breasts should be regular, not too large nor too small, and of the requisite number.

It goes without saying that the man should possess the same qualities. And Ghotakamakha is of the opinion that it is a sin to love a woman who has already been enjoyed by another man.

The efforts of the friends and family of the young man will be needed to conclude a good marriage, and the prospective bridegroom should not hesitate to ask the help and advice of the friends of the girl he hopes to gain.

These friends can be of invaluable help. They should criticize the faults and defects both actual and possible of all other wooers, and laud to the point of outright exaggeration the qualities of their friend. They should point out to the parents of the girl the excellent and virtuous record of his ancestors and of his present family, and they should describe his qualities and attributes in such a way as to enlist the sympathy of his future mother-in-law.

Or perhaps one of his friends could disguise himself as an astrologer and predict a brilliant future and great wealth for the aspiring lover, based on the fact that he possesses all the necessary marks of good luck on his body and that his stars were in good conjunction at his birth and that the Sun has a great and beneficial influence in his sign of the Zodiac. Others could also try and further his cause by arousing the jealousy of the mother of the girl, by telling her that the young man is besieged by proposals from rich families and that he could actually do much better for himself than marry her daughter.

Finally, one should only take a girl as wife, or give her in marriage, when one is completely assured of the fortune, horoscope, good qualities and background of the family. Because, Ghotaka-mukha writes, a man should never decide to marry in a moment of caprice, as for instance on a soft summer's evening when he is in the company of a beautiful and willing girl; and, above all, one should never marry a girl who sleeps, weeps, or is out of the house when one comes to ask her hand in marriage, or who is engaged to another man. One should also not enter into any kind of marital contract with:

A woman who is hidden by her family;—A woman with an ugly name;—A woman with a flat nose;—A woman with wide and flaring nostrils;—A woman who is flatchested;—A woman who is hunchbacked;—A woman with bow legs and crooked thighs;—A woman with a bulging and prominent forehead;—A woman who is. bald;—A woman who does not love chastity;—A woman who has been possessed by other men;—A woman who is in any way disfigured;—A woman who has already passed puberty;—A woman who is also a friend;—A younger sister;—A woman who is a *Varshakari* (that is, one whose palms of the hand and soles of the feet are continually damp with perspiration).

In the same way, many writers consider that a girl who is named after one of the twenty-seven stars, or who is called after a tree or a river, is worthless, as is any girl whose name ends in an *r* or an *l*. But again, many wise men say that a man can only be happy if he marries a woman he loves, and consequently one should only marry a girl if one is in love with her.

When a young girl arrives at a marriageable age, her parents should dress her in attractive and becoming clothes and take her everywhere where she may be easily seen. Every afternoon they should dress her elegantly and send her out with her companions to attend religious sacrifices, sportive events and weddings, and she should be elegantly dressed so that she may be seen to her best advantage. They should also welcome with friendly words and open hospitality people of a family may present to them as prospective suitors for their daughter. They should subtly introduce the subject of their marriageable daughter into the conversation and then produce her dressed in her most beautiful robes for them to see. Then they should wait until the prospective suitors fix a day to discuss marriage. On this auspicious day, the parents of the girl should invite the suitor's family to bathe and have dinner with them, and when the subject of marriage is brought up they should not display any vulgar haste, but simply dismiss the question, saying casually, 'Everything in its time,' and refuse to discuss the question further until much later.

When a young man has wooed a girl according to the traditions of his country, or according to his own desires, he should marry her legally following the precepts laid down by Manu regarding the four kinds of marriage.

To avoid the difficulties that often accompany intercaste marriages, parents should be careful to see that any social gatherings that their daughter may attend, such as games, weddings and religious ceremonies, should only be held within the caste and that no members of either a superior or inferior caste should be present.

For the sages condemn what is known as a 'Superior Alliance' in which the husband is forced to serve his wife and her powerful family as a kind of servant, or an 'Inferior Alliance' in which the man and his family look down on the lower-caste wife and treat her with cruelty and disrespect.

Only when a husband and wife respect and love one another, and when the parents of both parties concerned also respect each other, can a marriage be called an alliance in the true sense of the word.

Therefore, a man should not marry either above or below his station, but should marry a woman who has a similar economic and intellectual background.

CHAPTER 2

How to win the Confidence of a Virgin

During the first three days after the wedding, the man and the woman should sleep on hard wood boards and abstain from sexual pleasures. A little alkali or salt mixed into their food will render their continence easier. The next week they should bathe together to the sound of joyful instruments, dress and dine together and entertain their parents and other guests. These rules are appiicable to all the castes. On the tenth day, the husband should begin to talk softly and flatteringly to his wife, so as to calm her fears and inspire in her confidence and a desire for the sexual act.

There are even some learned men who state that to win a woman's confidence the husband should not speak with her for the first three days. But the disciples of Bhabravya wisely add that if a man is silent during the first three days, it is very possible that his young wife, disgusted at seeing him as mute and immobile as a marble column, will be disillusioned and come to despise him as a kind of emasculated eunuch.

Vatsyayana, on the other hand, is of the opinion that a man should start by inspiring his wife with confidence, but that he should abstain from sexual pleasure in the beginning.

Women have a gentle and timid nature, and they want to be approached with gentleness and consideration. If they are subjected to a brutal assault by a man they hardly know, they are apt to conceive a hatred of the sexual act and even sometimes a deep hatred of the entire male sex. The husband should therefore approach his bride with as much gentleness as she desires, and treat her with great kindness and consideration so that she is no longer afraid, and thus lead her subtly to the perilous brink of desire.

He should kiss her for the first time in a way which will please her the most, because this first kiss should be very short—a mere invitation.

He should embrace only the upper part of her body because this is the easiest and simplest of all embraces. If the woman is mature and the man has known her for some time, he may embrace her by the light of a lamp. But if she is very young, or if he hardly knows her, he should embrace her in total darkness. When the bride submits to this embrace, he should try and put a 'tambula' or betel nut leaf in her mouth. If she refuses, he must plead with her and try to convince her by flattery, vows of fidelity and subtle words to accept the gift. If she is still adamant he should kneel before her—for no matter how angry a woman is, she can never refuse a kneeling man. When she finally accepts the 'tambula,' the man should kiss her graciously, silently and gently on the mouth. This first step accomplished, the husband should engage his bride in conversation, and ask her questions about things he does not know or pretends for the sake of conversation not to know, and which require only a short reply. If through timidity she does not reply, he should once again ask her the same questions in a persuasive and gentle manner. If she still does not reply, he

56

should urge her to answer, for as Ghotakamukha has so wisely observed, 'all women listen to what a man says to them, but often they do not say a word themselves.'

If she is pressed to answer, the shy bride will probably reply with a shy nod of her head. Then he should take advantage of the situation and ask her if she loves him. At first she will not answer. Then, when repeatedly urged, she will finally timidly nod her head in acquiescence. If by any chance the husband has known his wife before the wedding, he should take advantage of this fact and have a long conversation with her through the intermediary of a friend, who, possessing the confidence of both the parties concerned, can tell one a lot about the other. And if by chance the friend happens to have revealed more to the husband than his bride wished, the husband can use this to his advantage now by mentioning the fact and adding, 'Your friend told me that you had said this or that about me.' To which the girl will hastily and shyly reply, 'I never said any such thing,' and smile and glance furtively at her husband.

If the wife is already known to her husband and is filled with desire for him, she can significantly place the tambula or garland of flowers near him without saying a word, or she can conceal the garland in the warmth of her bodice. Encouraged by her efforts, the husband should gently caress her firm young breasts, and if she tries to prevent him from continuing this subtle caress, he should say to her, 'I shall stop if you will kiss me,' and thereby lead her to embrace him once again. While she is embracing him, he should allow his hands to wander gently all over her body. Then, almost imperceptibly, he should draw her on to his knees and his caresses should become more and more urgent. If she refuses to yield to his desire, he should frighten her by saying:

'I shall bite and scratch you so hard that it will leave scars on your lips and on your breasts. Then I shall do the same on my body and I shall tell all our friends that you have done this. What will you say then?'

And in this way the husband should alternately threaten and calm his wife, as a parent threatens and persuades a child to obtain obedience, and so make her submit to his desires.

On the second and third night, when his bride is more assured and less timid, the man should caress her all over her body, then he should gently slide his hands down her silk-clothed thighs and rub the soft plump circle where the thigh joins the body. If she protests, he should innocently ask her, 'What harm is there in that?' and persuade her to let him continue. Once he has gained this point, he should gently touch the most secret and responsive parts of her body, untie the belt and knot of her robe, and lifting her underskirt he should caress her naked thighs and the soft dark angle between them. He should do all these things subtly and casually, but he should not as yet begin actual intercourse.

Thereafter, he should assure his bride further by telling her how much he loves her and how many hopes he has nourished concerning her. He should teach her the sixty-four arts, and promise to remain faithful to her and remove all her fears regarding other women, and slowly overcoming her timidity he should finally lead her to the ultimate act and enjoy her at first discreetly, in such a way as not to frighten her.

A man who conforms with the desires and inclinations of a young girl should attempt to win her obedience in such a way as to also win her love and confidence. One cannot succeed in winning a woman's affection and respect if one follows her whims blindly, nor if one opposes her constantly. One has to adopt a middle course.

He who knows how to make himself loved by women, protect their honor and gain their confidence, can be assured of their love and fidelity. But he who neglects a woman because she appears too timid receives only her scorn, because she looks on him as an uncivilized savage who does not know how to conquer and govern a woman.

On the other hand, a woman taken by force by a man she does not know and who does not understand the feminine heart, becomes a nervous, worried and depressed person. She begins to detest the man who raped her, and as a result of her frustrated affections and desires she rapidly sinks into despair and becomes an avowed enemy of the male sex; or even worse, if she particularly detests her husband she will turn to other men for comfort and so revenge herself on him.

CHAPTER 3

Courtship and the revelation of one's feelings by signs and acts

A poor man endowed with good qualities, a man born of a low class family and endowed with very mediocre talents, a rich neighbor and a man still under the tutelage of his father, his mother or his brothers, should not marry before they are sure that their betrothed loves and respects them since her childhood.

Thus a boy who has no parents, and lives with his uncle, should try and win his uncle's daughter or some other girl, even though she may have been previously promised to another man. This manner of winning a wife is morally irreproachable, according to Ghotakamukha, because one can acquire both Dharma and Artha as well by a marriage contracted in this way as by any other kind of marriage.

When a boy begins to court a girl he loves, he should pass his time with her and amuse her with different games and diversions suitable to her age and condition, such as picking and gathering flowers, weaving flower garlands, pretending to belong to an imaginary family, cooking appetizing dishes, playing dice, cards, the game of 'odd and even,' 'hunting the middle finger,' 'six pebbles,' and other similar games which are popular in the country and may please the young girl.

He should also organize community games in which many people can take part, such as hide-and-seek, and many athletic exercises or other games of this sort which can be played by the girl, her friends and servants.

The young man should also be careful to show a great deal of good will toward any older woman his beloved may admire, and above all he should win—by his kindness and many little services —the friendship of the daughter of his beloved's nurse. For even though the latter may guess that his interest in her has an ulterior motive, she will not stand in his way and may even help him to win his bride, and to this end, even though she may know his real character, she will praise him constantly to the family of the young girl.

The young man in his effort to please the woman of his choice should try and give her everything she desires. Thus he should give her rare gifts and toys that her other companions do not possess. For example, he can give her a multicolored ball and other curiosities of this sort. He can give her dolls made of cloth, wood, buffalo horn, ivory, wax, plaster or clay, or utensils for cooking, suggestive wooden figures—such as a man and a woman, a pair of rams, goats or sheep. Also miniature temples made of clay, bamboo or wood consecrated to different goddesses, cages of parrots, cuckoos, starlings, quail, cocks and partridges, vases in a variety of elegant forms, water-drawing machines, cithers and other musical instruments, wooden props for images, colored stools, lacquer, tilak, yellow mehendi, vermilion, and kajal or eye mascara, sandalwood, saffron and 'pan' made out of betel nuts and wrapped in betel leaves.

He should present these gifts on different occasions and they should also provide a good reason for meeting her often. Some of these presents should be made in public and some in private according to the circumstances. In other words, he should try and make her realize that he is ready to do anything she desires.

He should meet her in secret and tell her that he is afraid that her family and friends may not approve of him. He should also casually add that many of the gifts he gave her were very rare and much desired by others. When the young girl seems to like him better, he should tell her amusing stories—if she desires to be amused; or if she is impressed by conjurers he should show her some tricks; if she is curious to see the various arts he should not hesitate to show his proficiency in them—thus, if she loves song, he should sing for her, and on certain days when they go together to festivals or fairs, or when she comes home after a visit to some relatives, he should offer her bouquets of flowers, ornaments for her head and ears, and rings, for it is on such occasions that gifts should be given.

He should also teach her nurse's daughter the sixty-four arts as practiced by men, and thus indirectly let his beloved know how good he is in the art of sexual pleasure.

During his courtship the young man should take particular pains to dress well and be as courteous and charming as possible, for young girls like young men who are constantly with them to be handsome, pleasant, and well-dressed. Women, though they may love a man, make no effort to conquer the object of their affections, and it would be idle to wait for them to declare the true nature of their feelings.

Yet it is not impossible to discover the truth of a young girl's feelings; being as yet innocent and unschooled, they often betray themselves unconsciously. Here are some exterior signs which invariably betray the love of a young girl.

She never looks her loved one in the face, and blushes when he looks at her. Under some pretext or other she lets him get a glimpse of her ankles and arms. She looks at him secretly when his back is turned, and bows her head and answers indistinctly if he asks her a direct question. She likes to be in his company and speaks to her servants in a very special way to attract his attention if he is not looking at her. She never seems to want to leave his company, and tells him long stories very slowly as if she never wanted the conversation to end. She kisses and caresses a child in his presence, and draws ornamental symbols on the foreheads of her servants. She also takes care to be more quick and graceful than usual, especially if her servants speak to her jokingly in the presence of her lover. She confides in the friends of her lover and shows them respect and deference. She is good to her servants, speaks with them and orders them to do their work as if she were their mistress, and listens to them attentively when she hears them discuss her lover with someone else. She eagerly goes to the house of her nurse's daughter and arranges to see her lover there through the connivance of the former. She never lets her loved one see her when she is not carefully dressed, and she sends him her ring, earrings or her garland of flowers through a friend. She constantly wears some ornament that he has given her and is very sad when her parents speak of another suitor before her, and she avoids the friends and supporters of the latter.

A man who has noticed and correctly read the feelings of a young girl towards him, and who has accurately estimated her affection for him by a close observation of her movements and gestures should do everything possible to unite with this girl.

He should in general capture the affection of a very young girl by childish games, that of a slightly older girl by his proficiency in the arts, and that of a woman who loves him by having recourse to friends who are in her confidence.

CHAPTER 4

Things which a man must do alone to assure Union. Also things which a girl must do to acquire domination and control over a man

When a young girl begins to demonstrate her interest and affection by the subtle ways described in the last chapter, her lover should try to conquer her entirely.

In the games and sports in which they both take part, he should touch her hand as often as possible. And when alone, he should embrace and caress her in the many ways described in the beginning of the book. He should show her human figures carved out of leaves and other suggestive symbols of this nature. When they go swimming the young lover should dive far away from his beloved and then suddenly appear quite close to her so that their damp bodies accidentally touch. The young lover should appear to be deeply affected by the sight of spring leaves and other budding things and he should repeatedly describe to her in a touching manner the torments he endures for her.

In the parties and assemblies organized by members of his caste he should sit close to the girl and touch her secretly. He should place his foot on hers and caress all her toes, and if she does not object he should then venture to take her foot in his hand and repeat the same caresses. And when the young maiden washes his feet he should gently press one of her fingers between his toes . . . in fact, whenever he is in her presence, all his gestures, expressions and acts should express the intensity of his passion.

He should pour the water he receives to rinse his mouth as a libation at her feet, and if he finds himself alone with her in some dimly lit corner he must make love to her without in any way frightening or hurting her.

Every time he finds himself seated next to her, he should murmur, 'I have something very important to tell you,' and when she consents to meet him alone he should express his love for her more by gestures and gentle caresses than by words. And when he is sure of her feelings towards him, he should pretend to be ill and ask her to come to him to visit him. Then when she is standing by his bed, he should take her hand and place it on his brow and ask her to prepare some drug for him, saying, 'It is you and no one else who must do this work for me.' And when she is about to leave he should beg her to return the next day. This pretended illness should last two or three days. And, as a result, she will get used to coming to his house, and he should take care to have long conversations with her. For as Ghotakamukha says: 'No matter how passionately a man may love a woman he will only conquer her after a great investment of words.'

At last when the young lover is sure that he has completely won his beloved can he start to enjoy her.

It has been said that women are less timid in the evening, in the night and in dark and dimly lit rooms, and that darkness tends to excite their passions and arouse their desire for love, and therefore men should possess a woman only during these hours. But this is, of course, sheer nonsense. A woman in love is ready for intercourse at any time of the day or night.

If, however, a young man cannot arrive at the desired end himself, he should send the daughter of his nurse or a friend of his loved one to bring her to him without telling her where they are taking her. Then he should press his advantage in the above manner as urgently as possible. Or he can send his own servant to work for her, and she can then sing his praises all day and thereby facilitate the conquest.

Thus when he is sure of her reciprocal love, by her behavior towards him at festivals, fairs, theaters, public gatherings, ceremonies, weddings and on other such occasions, he can begin to take his pleasure of her when they are alone. For if a man approaches a woman at the right time and in the right place she is rarely unfaithful.

A young girl who is endowed with excellent qualities, well educated and beautiful, though without a fortune and born from a family of an inferior caste, or an orphan who nevertheless follows the laws and traditions of her caste, should try and marry a young, handsome, talented and rich man, or any other that she can persuade to marry her through weakness or without the consent of his parents. To this end she should employ all her art to make herself loved and desired, and should seek out all possible opportunities to meet and be seen by her chosen lover. Her mother should also do all in her power to further her aims and enlist the help of companions and friends if necessary. The young girl should arrange to frequently find herself alone with her lover and should make him gifts of betel nut, flowers, 'pan,' and perfumes. She should also demonstrate her ability in the arts, performing soothing massages, in love bites and scratches, and in the science of arousing desire through subtle pressures on various parts of the body. Finally she should be able to discuss subjects which interest him, and should often lead the conversation round to the subject of love.

But all the ancient sages agree on one point: no matter how much a woman loves a man she should never offer herself to him or make the initial overtures to sexual intercourse, because a woman who behaves in this way exposes herself to ridicule, scorn, and refusal. Only when a man expresses his desire for her, should she show her affection for him and allow him to embrace her without any alarm or excitement as if she did not quite understand what he desired.

When he wishes to kiss her more passionately she should gently repulse his embrace, and when he begs her to allow him to make love to her, she should refuse, but still allow him to caress the sensitive and secret parts of her body. No matter how much he importunes her she should never submit willingly but resist to the last moment, and only when she is completely sure of her lover's passion, his sincerity, and his fidelity should she ultimately allow him to take her, making sure however that he will marry her promptly.

A girl who is much sought after should marry a man she loves and whom she thinks she is able to obey and please. But if because of their own interests her parents force her to marry a rich man without being concerned about the appearance and character of the man, or if they give her to a man with many wives, she will never love her husband, even though he may be rich, handsome, virile, powerful, and healthy, and desirous of pleasing her in every way.

A considerate husband who is still master of his house, though he may be poor and not unduly handsome, is preferable to a man who is shared by several women, no matter how handsome or rich he may be. Women who are married to rich men with several wives never give themselves completely to their husbands and never trust them, and though they may enjoy all the superficial luxuries of life they nevertheless betray their husbands and seek their fulfillment with other men.

On the other hand, a man who is vulgar or fallen from his social position and much given to travel does not deserve a wife; and the same is true of the man who having a wife and children spends all his time at sports and rarely comes home to his family.

Of all the suitors that a girl might have, the only one who is really her husband is the one who possesses the qualities she admires, for only such a man can ever have real superiority and control over her because he is the husband of her love.

CHAPTER 5

Different forms of Marriage

If a young girl cannot meet her lover often enough, she should send the daughter of her nurse to see him, assuming of course that she trusts her confidante and is sure of her loyalty.

In her conversation with her mistress' lover, the young confidante should praise her mistress' beauty, character, talents, poise, maturity and tenderness, but she should never allow the young man to suspect that she has been sent for this purpose. On her return she should praise the young man highly to her mistress . . . taking care to say things she knows her enamored mistress would like to hear. She should also speak slightingly of other suitors, and criticize the miserliness and indiscretion of their parents and the insignificance of their families. She should further cite the classical examples of happy matrimony such as Sakuntala—who, having married a young man of her choice and of her caste, was always happy and respected in her community. She should also warn her mistress not to be misled by the temptation of wealth by telling her of the numerous young girls who, married to wealthy and powerful men, were soon made miserable by the jealousy and venom of rival wives. In other words she should praise the prosperity, chastity, obedience, and affection of the young man in question and calm her mistress' superstitious fear that some ill luck may follow the marriage.

For, in questions of legal marriage, the nurse's daughter often acts as a go-between, instructing the young girl in the ways of love, the habits of men, and in particular, the peculiarities and habits of the young man in question, repeating daily, 'Ah, if the young man kidnapped you, it would be the best thing that could ever happen.'

When a young girl has finally succumbed to her desire and lives with a man as his wife, the lover should order a brazier of sacred fire from a Brahmin, and after having strewn the ground with a certain plant he should offer a sacrifice to the fire and marry the girl in accordance with the principles of religious law. Then, and only then, should he inform the parents, for in the eyes of the older generation a marriage contracted before the sacred flame can never be annulled.

After the consummation of the wedding, the parents of the groom should be informed that their son has acquired a wife, and the parents of the bride should also be tactfully informed, so that they will ultimately give their consent and forgive the secretive way in which the marriage was celebrated. Once they have accepted the idea of the marriage, the two families should have a formal reconciliation and offer each other gifts. This is the way a man should marry a woman according to the Ghandharva rite and traditions.

If a young girl cannot make up her mind, or if she does not wish to say that she is willing to marry, her lover can achieve this end in the following ways:

1) At the first opportunity, he should ask a friend he trusts and, more important, whom the girl also trusts, to bring his loved one to his house on some pretext. Once the girl has innocently been

led into his house, he should hastily send for some sacred fire and conclude the Ghandharva ceremony.

2) If, however, the young lover hears that his chosen bride is about to be married to someone else very soon, he should do everything in his power to influence her mother and discredit her daughter's fiancé in her eyes. If he succeeds he should prevail on the mother to lead her daughter to a neighbor's house, where he will have the sacred fire and other necessities ready for the marriage ceremony.

3) The young man should cultivate the brother of the woman he desires, especially if they are of the same age. He should help him with all his amorous intrigues and together they should visit the most beautiful and talented courtesans. When the young man has become his fast friend—and it is well known that young people are willing to lay down their lives for their friends who are of the same age and have the same tastes as they—he should confide his love for his sister and ask his help. Then he should leave it to the brother to entice his sister to some place where the Ghandharva ceremony can be quickly performed.

4) On the next festive occasion the young lover should make the nurse's daughter administer a drug to her young mistress. Then he should carry the drugged girl to some quiet place and enjoy her before the effect of the potion has worn off. After he has possessed her, he should send for the sacred fire and marry her.

5) Similarly, with the connivance of the nurse's daughter, he should carry off the girl he desires when she is sleeping and take her while she is still asleep. When she awakes she will have lost her virginity and he can then proceed with the official ceremony.

6) If the young lover knows that the woman he wishes to marry is going on a short trip, or is out walking in a park or a garden, he should ask some of his friends to help him and together they should kidnap the young girl and force her into the marriage ceremony.

However, the sages note that it is better to perform the sacred ceremony before carnal intercourse than after. If, however, this is not possible, then it is no sin to have recourse to other methods which lead to the same end.

As the object of all marriage is love, the Ghandharva ceremony is respected, even if it has been performed under the most unfavorable circumstances, because it fulfills this purpose.

In fact, one of the great attributes of this form of marriage is that it brings happiness, causes less fuss and expense than the other more 'correct' forms of marriage and is usually the culmination of a deep mental and physical attachment between two people.

PART FOUR

THE WIFE

CHAPTER 1

The life of a virtuous woman and her behavior during her husband's absence

A virtuous woman who loves her husband should always act in perfect obedience to his wishes and desires as if he were a kind of divine being, and with his permission she should take upon herself the complete responsibility for the family and the household. Moreover, she should avoid the company of beggars, Buddhists, loose women, knaves, fortune tellers and sorcerers.

She should see that the whole house is kept clean; that there are flowers of many different colors in each room, and that the colors of the flowers harmonize with the colors of the room; that the floor is polished and gleaming, so that the whole house gives an air of respectability and cleanliness.

The wife should also make sure that all the various ingredients necessary for morning, afternoon and evening prayers are kept ready for use in the courtyard of the house. Moreover, she herself should honor the household Gods and see to it that all the rites accompanying their worship are scrupulously observed. She must also observe all the fasting and religious vows of her husband, and if he should try to stop her, she should beg him to allow her to continue. For as Gonardiya observes, nothing makes the head of the household more beholden to his wife than the strict observance of all the religious rites.

The attitude of the wife towards the parents, relatives, friends and servants of her husband should be conditioned by the rank and merit of the above individuals.

In the garden, she should cultivate green vegetables, feather-topped forests of sugar cane, figs, fennel, parsley and yellow mustard seed. She should also plant fragrant flowers, grouping their colors harmoniously against a background of trees. Jasmine, yellow

67

amaryllis, and tea roses are some of the most fragrant and beautiful of flowers. The garden should also contain flowering arbors and little rustic seats, and in the center an ornamental lotus pool or fountain.

The wife must always take her husband's tastes into account when planning the menus, and should avoid any dishes that might upset him or make him ill. The kitchen should be in a quiet part of the building, as far from the living quarters as possible, and no stranger should ever be allowed to cross its threshold.

As soon as she hears her lord's footsteps, she should instantly leave whatever she has been doing and rise, ready to obey his slightest desire. Then she must order her servants to wash his feet if she does not do so herself.

Every time she accompanies her husband to a feast or social gathering, she should dress herself carefully in her finest ornaments; and she must never invite anyone, or accept any invitations to attend weddings, sacrifices, visit temples or go out with her friends without his consent. She should also always ask his permission first if she wishes to participate in any games or sports.

The wife, moreover, must always sit after her husband is seated, and rise before he does, and she should never wake him when he sleeps.

If her husband has behaved badly or been unfaithful, the good wife should never blame or scold him too bitterly, no matter how angry she may feel or how much she may have suffered. She should never use harsh language, but should gently reproach him, taking care not to anger him and tempering her reproaches with conciliatory words. Above all, she must not be quarrelsome, for as Gonardiya correctly observes: 'Nothing disgusts a man more than this fault in women.'

The virtuous wife should avoid speaking evil of anyone, talking in whispers, scowling, spying on passers-by through the keyhole, gossiping in public squares and staying for hours in deserted places. But above all, she should always keep her teeth, body, hair, and in fact her entire person, clean, neat and elegant.

When a wife desires union with her husband, she should dress herself in an ornate costume, put flowers in her hair, and wear vivid and exciting colors, and perfume herself heavily with unguents and ointments.

But the costume she wears daily should be simple, light and of good quality, and she should use perfumes, jewels and flowers with great discretion.

At certain seasons of the year, when these things are cheap, she should buy clay, bamboo, sandalwood, skins, iron vases and also oil and salt. Odorous herbs and ointments, medicines, and other things that are constantly needed must also be bought and stored away in a secret place in the house. Also radish, sweet potatoes, beetroot, mango, cucumber, mad-apple, pumpkin, garlic and onion seeds, as well as other vegetables, should be bought and sown in their respective seasons.

A married woman should never reveal the exact extent of her wealth to strangers, nor should she reveal the confidences that her husband has entrusted to her.

She should surpass all other women of equal rank in poise, goodness, knowledge of cooking, dignity of bearing, and the manner in which she serves her husband.

The expenses of the year should be subtracted from profits and not from capital. The milk left over after a meal should be converted into clarified butter. Oil and sugar should be prepared at home, and cloth should also be woven and spun in the home. There should always be enough rope and string in the house, as well as strips of bark that can later be woven into rope.

The wife should also supervise the cleansing of rice, and she must know how to employ the rice and the chaff for diverse purposes.

She must be responsible for paying the salaries of the servants, supervising the cultivation of the fields, the flocks, the construction of carts, and she should take special care of the rams, cocks, quails, parrots, starlings, cuckoos, peacocks, monkeys and deer, and lastly she should control the revenue and expenditure for the day. She should give her old clothes to servants who work well as a sign of her appreciation, and she should be generous towards her staff and reward them with gifts on festive occasions. But she must never give away anything without first asking her husband.

The drums in which wine is made must be carefully inspected, and she must be directly responsible for everything that is bought or sold.

When friends of her husband come to visit the house, she should greet them graciously, offering them flowers, perfumes, incense, and 'pan' (betel nut wrapped in betel nut leaf).

She must always treat her mother- and father-in-law with deference, bowing always to their will and never contradicting them. She should not converse too much with them, but on the other hand never be cold towards them. She must never laugh loudly in their presence, and should treat their friends and enemies in the same way as she treats her own. Moreover, the virtuous woman must not be vain, nor too occupied with personal pleasures.

When her husband is away from home, the virtuous wife should only wear propitious ornaments of good fortune, and she should fast and observe all the rites of worship even more scrupulously than before. No matter how anxious or worried she may be, she must not neglect her household tasks. She should ask the eldest women of her household to come and sleep near her, and she should do everything possible to make herself agreeable to them. She must clean and care for the objects cherished by her husband, and finish any work begun by him. While she is alone she should not visit friends and relatives unless it is for some special reason, such as a feast or a funeral, and then she should dress very simply and be accompanied by her servants and not stay long. She should observe the feasts and fasts with the consent of the oldest members of the household, and she should increase the family capital by undertaking carefully planned business ventures through the intermediary of honest servants whom she can trust. For during her husband's absence, she should try to earn as much and spend as little as possible. And when her husband returns, she should greet him in the simple unadorned costume she has worn during his absence, so that he can see how she has conducted herself. She should offer him some gifts, and prepare the necessary ingredients for a thanksgiving sacrifice to the Gods.

A woman, whether she comes of a noble family, or is a virgin widow remarried, or a concubine, should lead a chaste life, be devoted to her husband, and always be concerned about his well-being.

Women who lead this kind of life, acquire Dharma, Artha and Kama, win a high position, and obtain the love, respect and gratitude of their husbands.

CHAPTER 2

Rules of conduct for the first wife towards the other wives of her husband: of the youngest wife towards the older wives; the behavior of a widowed virgin who has remarried; of a wife rejected by her husband; women of the King's harem; and the conduct of a man who has more than one wife

Men take a second wife for the following reasons: 1) Madness or evil nature of the first wife;—2) Physical distaste for his present wife;—3) Lack of children;—4) No son to continue the name;—5) Incontinence on the part of the husband.

From the very beginning of the marriage, the wife should try to win her husband's heart by her devotion, good humor and wisdom. If, however, she does not conceive, she must herself advise her husband to take a second wife. And when the second wife has been married and comes to the house to live, the first wife should give her a superior position in the household and look on her as a sister.

In the morning the older woman should help the younger to dress herself in the presence of their husband, and she should not be jealous of the attentions the husband pays to his new bride.

If the younger wife does something foolish and displeases the husband, the elder wife should at once come to her assistance, give her good advice and teach her how to conduct herself before her husband.

The first wife should treat the children of the second as if they were her own, be more considerate with her servants than with her own, and be loving and gentle with the friends of the other and honor her parents greatly.

If, however, there are more than two wives, the first wife should make an ally of the second, and together they should try and cause a quarrel between the latest wife and the one who last enjoyed her husband's special favors. Then they should gather the other women around them and denounce the youngest wife as wicked and intriguing. If this young favorite happens, however, to quarrel with the husband, the oldest wife should under the guise of sympathy and good advice encourage her to do everything contrary to her husband's wishes and so make matters much worse. If it is only a lover's quarrel, the first wife should do everything in her power to create a really serious rift. But if, in spite of everything, she sees that the husband continues to love his young favorite, she should change her tactics to avoid her husband's displeasure and bring about a reconciliation.

How the youngest wife should behave towards the eldest

The youngest wife should regard the first wife as a mother and never give anything, even to her parents, without first informing her. She should confide in her completely and never have intercourse with the husband without first asking her permission. She must never reveal anything the eldest wife has confided to her, and she should take better care of the first wife's children than of her own.

When she is alone with her husband she should serve him well, but never complain of the sorrow that her rival causes her.

She can take advantage of her position and try to obtain some special favor from her husband by telling him that she lives only for him and for the affection that he gives her. But she should never confide her love for her husband nor the husband's love for her to anyone, because a woman who reveals the secrets of the bedroom risks being scorned and rejected as a worthless gossip.

Gonardiya advises a young wife to ask her husband for particular favors only when they are alone, because if she does so in the presence of others, she incurs the jealousy and hatred of the first wife.

If, however, the first wife has been rejected by the husband or is sterile, she should treat her with sympathy and beg the husband to be good to the unfortunate woman, but she must all the same try and outshine her example by leading a virtuous and chaste life.

The widowed virgins

A poor widow, or one who has a weak character and remarries for the second time, is known as a twice married widow.

The disciples of Bhabravya state that a widowed virgin should never marry a man she may later be forced to leave, either because of his bad character, or because he lacks the qualities essential to a man.

Gonardiya is of the opinion that if a widow remarries it is in the hope of finding happiness, and as happiness depends on the good qualities of the husband and the pleasures of love-making, a virgin widow should take care to choose a man who possesses these qualities.

At the marriage the widow should ask her husband for money to pay for the drinks offered to the guests, the refreshments and dinners for the family and the presents she has had to give to friends and helpers; or if she prefers, she can pay these expenses herself. In the same way, she can either wear the jewels of her husband's family or her own.

As to the exchange of gifts and presents there is no fixed rule, but if she leaves her husband of her own accord afterwards she must return all that she has received from him. But if she is driven out of the house by her husband, she has the right to keep everything she has received.

After the wedding she will live in her husband's house as one of the chief members of the family, but she must treat the other women with kindness, be generous to the servants, and greet all the friends of the house with friendliness and good humor.

She should prove to her husband that she is better versed in the sixty-four arts than the other women of the household, and if she quarrels with her lord and master she must not be harsh to him but, on the contrary, do everything to please him and soften his mood by practicing the sixty-four methods of sensual pleasure.

She should be obliging to the other wives of her husband, give presents to their children and instruct them in the arts of life and make them gifts of jewels and toys. But she should place her trust more securely in the friends and servants of her husband than in his other wives. Lastly, she must always be eager to go to drinking parties, picnics, fairs and festivals and, in fact, accompany her husband in a continued round of pleasure.

The woman who is not loved by her husband

A woman who is not loved by her husband and who suffers from the persecution of the other wives should ally herself with the current favorite of the husband, who will help her and teach her all the arts she knows herself.

She should act as a nurse to his children and cultivate his friends. When she has won their confidence, she should persuade them to tell her husband how much she loves him.

During religious ceremonies, sacred vows, fasts and feasts, she should play a leading rôle without forming too good an opinion of herself.

When her husband is lying on his bed she must never approach him, unless she is sure that it will please him, and she should never reproach him if he does not desire or take her.

If her husband quarrels with another wife she will do her best to reconcile them; and if the husband wishes to meet his mistress she will offer to arrange the rendezvous.

She must try to discover the weaknesses of her husband, but she must never reveal her knowledge, and in general should behave in such a way that her husband can nevertheless consider her a good and devoted wife.

The King and the Royal harem

Three kinds of women are employed in the Royal harem.

The *Kanchukiyas* are servants in the service of the Queens. In olden times, they always covered their breasts with a cloth known as *Kanchuki,* while the Queens were always naked to the waist.

The *Mahallarikas* are the women who have authority over the servants of the harem.

73

The *Mahallikas* are also women with a certain authority.

The women must offer flowers, perfumes and rich garments to the King and on behalf of his wives.

In the afternoon, the King, dressed in the splendor of his ceremonial robes, visits the women of his harem who await him dressed in their most beautiful jewels. After having assigned to each one her special place and having given each Queen a special token of his affection, he converses with them all.

Then he visits the widowed virgins he has wed, and after them the concubines and the dancers. He does not visit these women collectively, but goes to see each one separately in her room.

When the King awakens from his afternoon's siesta, the woman who is in charge of selecting his wife for the night comes to visit him. She is accompanied by the followers of the wife whose turn it is to spend the night with him, by the followers of a wife whose turn was missed by mistake, and the followers of a wife who was indisposed when her turn came round. These followers offer ointments and perfumes sent by these wives to the King, and each one bears the signet ring of her mistress. The servants plead the cause of each of these Queens in turn, and the King accepts the gifts from one of them. The Queen is then informed that her turn has come.

At festivals, concerts and public ceremonies, all the King's wives are treated with respect and refreshments are offered to them.

But none of these royal wives is ever allowed to go out unaccompanied, and no woman whose character is not well-known and attested for is allowed to enter the harem.

A man who has several wives must be loyal to all of them. He must not be too indulgent nor too severe in regard to their faults, and must never tell one about the love, passion, physical imperfections or sexual weaknesses of the others. He should never discuss his various wives, and if one of them starts to complain about another, he should cut her short by informing her that she has exactly the same faults and defects.

He can please one wife by confiding in her, another by paying her a particular attention, a third by subtle flattery, and all of them by taking them to the public gardens, amusing them, giving them gifts, honoring their families, confiding in them, and above all by demonstrating his aptitude and pleasure in sexual union.

In conclusion, a young woman who is happy and willing and who follows the precepts of female conduct laid down in the Scriptures can be assured of her husband's love and preference over his other wives.

PART FIVE

THE WIVES OF OTHERS

CHAPTER 1

The chief characteristics of men and women, and why women resist the propositions of men. Men who are successful with women, and women who are easy to conquer

Under special and particular circumstances a man is allowed—without incurring moral demerit and reproach—to propose to the wife of another. But a sensible man must first carefully examine all the problems involved in such a situation. For instance, how easy or difficult is it to possess a certain woman, her aptitude for such a love affair, the dangers involved, and the far-reaching results of this union.

For instance, it is quite legitimate for a man to pursue another's wife because he and his life are in danger, if he cannot live without her and the intensity of his passion increases from day to day.

The gradual intensity of sexual passion can be divided into ten phases, which, once again, can be identified by the following symptoms:

1) Physical attraction;—2) Mental and spiritual communion;—3) Constant thought;—4) Sleeplessness;—5) Lack of appetite and loss of weight;—6) No interest in pleasures and amusements;—7) Complete disregard for modesty and prudence;—8) Madness; 9) Weakness;—10) Death.

The ancient authors say that a young man should gauge the consideration, disposition, sincerity, purity and instincts of the young woman as well as the intensity or feebleness of her passion by observing the shape of her body and certain significant signs and birthmarks.

But Vatsyayana is of the opinion that such physical indications are misleading and one should only judge women by their be-

75

havior and the physical expression of their thoughts and desires
ı their movements.

Gonikaputra affirms that in general a woman falls in love with
every handsome man she meets, just as a man feels attracted by
and desires to possess every beautiful woman he sees, but in most
cases this instantaneous attraction does not go any further, due to
a variety of reasons.

It is also true that women are more disinterested in their affections than are men. A woman loves blindly, without studying the
pros and cons of the case or looking into the right and wrong
of the situation, and she does not try to win a man with the idea
of achieving some ulterior objective.

A woman who is pursued by a man naturally repulses and refuses him, even though she may want nothing more than to give
herself to him. To finally gain her consent the lover must renew
his efforts to win her many times and convince her of his devotion and love.

ℐℯ is unusual for a man on the other hand to be even deeply in
ıove. Moral considerations and wisdom control his emotions and
keep them within the bounds of reason. And, even though he
may think constantly about the woman he desires, he does not
easily submit to the efforts she makes to conquer him.

Sometimes he himself makes a great effort to win a woman, but
if he fails he lets the matter drop and does not think about it any
more. And often after he has successfully possessed and enjoyed
a woman he loses all interest in her and, as is commonly known,
a man is not interested in that which is too easily gained. He enjoys the chase, the struggle, and always prefers a conquest which
has been difficult to achieve.

On the other hand, a woman refuses and repulses the amorous
propositions of a man for the following reasons:

1) Affection for her husband;—2) Desire for legal progeny;—
3) Lack of opportunity;—4) Anger at being approached too fa-
miliarly;—5) Difference of social rank;—6) Insecurity due to the
fact that men are known to love to travel from one woman to another;—7) Suspicion that her suitor is already involved with another woman;—8) Fear that the man will not keep his intentions
secret;—9) The thought that the man is too attached to his friends
and has too much consideration for them;—10) Apprehension that
he is not serious;—11) A feeling of inadequacy because he is a famous personality;—12) Fear that he is sexually too strong or too
passionate, in the case of the doe woman;—13) A feeling of shame
because he is too experienced and polished in these affairs;—
14) Memory of having once shared a deep platonic friendship with

him;—15) Scorn for his lack of worldly wisdom;—16) Distrust in his evil nature;—17) Indignation because he does not seem to be aware of her sincere love for him;—18) In the case of the elephant woman, the fear that the lover is a mare and possesses a very small sexual capacity;—19) Fear that she may do him harm;—20) Insecurity as regards herself and her shortcomings;—21) Fear of discovery;—22) Disillusionment in discovering he has grey hairs or a sly manner;—23) Fear that she will be put in the position of proving her chastity to her husband;—24) Suspicion that he is too morally scrupulous to undertake such a love affair without suffering from feelings of guilt.

Whatever the reason may be for refusing herself, the man should try and discover the cause of her reluctance at the very beginning, and try to overcome it.

Thus any shame she may feel because of her social position or her talents he can dispel by giving her proof of his sincere passion and desire for her.

If she complains that the possibilities of meeting are very limited, he should immediately counter her objection by providing her with an easy solution.

If she is in awe of him, he can overcome her timidity by treating her with great familiarity.

If she suspects him of possessing a bad character, he should prove his worth and vision to her.

If she accuses him of indifference, he must multiply his efforts; and if she is afraid, he must gently encourage her to take the ultimate step.

The men who are usually successful with women are the following:

1) Men who are very accomplished in the science of love;—2) Those who can tell amusing and exciting stories well;—3) Men who have been used to living with women since their infancy;—4) Those who can win their confidence;—5) Men who give gifts generously;—6) Smooth and eloquent talkers;—7) Those who take care to consider and please feminine tastes;—8) Men who have never loved another woman before;—9) Men who act as go-betweens;—10) Men who observe and recognize feminine weaknesses;—11) Those who are sought after by honest and respectable women;—12) Men who are on good terms with the friends of the woman in question;—13) Those who have an air of well-being; 14) Men who have been brought up with women;—15) Neighbors;—16) Men who are much given to sexual pleasures, even if it be only with their servants;—17) The lovers of the confidante; —18) Recently married men;—19) Men who love picnics and

parties;—20) Men of a liberal and broad-minded disposition;—21) Those reputed to be very strong and passionate (the bulls);—22) Brave and audacious men;—23) Men who outshine the husbands of the desired women in appearance, character and liberality;—24) Those who dress magnificently and live in great luxury.

And the women who most easily seduced are the following:

1) Those who always stand at the door of their house;—2) Women who spend their time watching the life of the street;—3) Those who spend the day gossiping next door;—4) A woman who stares directly and boldly into the eyes of men;—5) A go-between;—6) A woman who casts glances slyly;—7) A woman whose husband has married again for no valid reason;—8) A woman who detests her husband, or who is hated by him;—9) One who has no one to watch over her and look after her;—10) A childless woman;— 11) One whose family or caste are not well-known;—12) A woman who has lost her children;—13) One who in public makes a great show of being very devoted and affectionate to her husband;—14) A woman who loves society;—15) The widow of an actor;—16) A widow;—17) A woman in need of money;—18) One who loves sensual pleasures;—19) The wife of a man who has many brothers younger than himself;—20) A vain woman;—21) A woman whose husband is inferior to her in talent and rank;—22) A woman who is worried by the mad behavior of her husband;—23) One who was married as a child to a rich man, and who on growing up discovers that she does not love him, but is looking for a man more to her tastes;—24) A wife who is mistreated by her husband for no just reason;—25) One who is not respected by other women of the same rank and beauty as herself;—26) A woman whose husband travels a lot;—27) A jeweler's wife;—28) A jealous woman;—29) A greedy woman;—30) An immoral woman;—31) A sterile woman;—32) A lazy woman;—33) A cowardly woman;—34) One with a hump on her back;—35) A dwarf;—36) A cheat;—37) A vulgar woman;—38) One who emits a bad odor;—39) A sick woman;—40) An old woman.

> Nature sows the seed of Desire in man's heart;
> The refinement of art develops the wild seed
> And wisdom guards it from all dangers
> Until it flowers and grows strong and sure,
> For a man who is skillful in the arts of love
> And who studies the ways of women carefully
> And seeks to please, flatter, and love them
> Is generally successful and content in their company.

CHAPTER 2

*Ways of addressing a woman and the efforts
necessary to conquer her*

The ancient sages believe that virgins are more easily seduced when approached directly by the man himself than through the intercession of friends or messengers; while married women'are more likely to comply if wooed by an intermediary or a go-between.

However, the author of this work believes that a man should always approach the woman he desires in his own person, and only if this is impossible should he have recourse to a friend or a go-between. Moreover, it is quite untrue to generalize and state that bold and experienced women are more likely to succumb to the impassioned plea of a lover, while inexperienced and timid girls can better be approached through an intermediary.

Now when a man desires to court a woman, he should first make the acquaintance of the beloved in the following way:

Arrange to be seen by the woman he desires at some ordinary or special occasion. If the meeting takes place at the home of one or the other it can be said to be an ordinary occasion; but if they meet at a neighbor's house, or in the home of a member of the same caste, or at the residence of a minister or a doctor, at a wedding, festival, sacrifice, funeral, or at a garden party, it can be said to be a special occasion.

No matter when or where they meet, the man should instantly convey to the woman the strength of his feelings by certain physical manifestations, such as pulling at his mustaches: staring at her meaningfully, clicking his nails, playing with his jewels, biting his lower lip, and other signs of the same sort. When she returns his gaze, he should turn to his friends and loudly discuss her and other women and he should show himself to be broad-minded and a lover of pleasure. If he happens to be seated next to a woman he knows, he should yawn, fidget, frown, and speak very slowly as if he were tired and listen to her remarks with evident boredom and indifference. He can also conduct a subtle conversation with a child or a young person, so that his remarks seem to apply to a third person but in reality are directed at the object of his affections. To excite her desire and interest he should kiss and embrace a child in her presence, gently push some betel nut into its mouth with his own tongue, pinch its cheek and chin caressingly, all the while stealing meaningful glances at his beloved.

The man can also caress a child which is seated on the knees of the woman and offer him a toy, which he can later reclaim. He can thus start a conversation with her about the child, and introduce himself to her. He should also take care to make himself agreeable to her relatives.

Once he has made friends with the desired woman he can use this friendship as an excuse to visit her home frequently. During these visits he should casually touch on the subject of love. . . she will then surely leave the room, but not so far that she cannot hear the rest of the conversation.

As the friendship develops he should leave something in her care and come frequently to inspect or withdraw a part of this object, or he can make her small gifts such as perfumed ointments or betel nut.

After this he should do everything in his power to introduce her to his wife, and encourage them to exchange confidences and sit with them in quiet and secluded places. To be able to see her more frequently he must see to it that both families patronize the same jeweler, basket-maker, dyer and laundry. And he should pay her long visits, pretending that he has some business he must discuss with her, or any other reason he can invent. And one thing should lead to another in such a way as to keep them constantly in contact with each other. If, for instance, she is in need of money or wishes to learn a certain art he should subtly suggest to her that he is willing to serve her in any way and is also able to lend her money or teach what she desires to learn.

He should enter into lively discussions with her when they are among friends on diverse subjects, and also examine works of art, jewels and precious stones. During these discussions he should show her rare objects that he knows she has never seen before, and if she argues with him and contradicts him, he should not retaliate, but assure her that she is right and that he shares the same opinion.

If, after some time, she becomes used to his presence and she indicates her interest and affection for him by diverse signs and movements of her body, the man should be encouraged to make every effort and do his best to possess her. But as young girls are not experienced in sexual matters, the man must approach the subject with great delicacy, taking care not to shock or frighten her. These precautions, of course, are not necessary with women who are already experienced in these matters.

Once a young maiden's intentions are clear and she has in

some measure forsaken her modesty, the man must begin to give her expensive gifts and the couple should exchange rings, clothes and flowers. She should also make him a symbolic gift of 'pan'; and if they are together at a festive gathering he should ask her to give him the flower in her hair or the one she holds in her hand. On the other hand, if he offers her a flower, the bloom should have a delicate perfume and should be marked by certain signs he has made with his fingers and teeth. Gradually he should overcome her fears, then one day lead her to some quiet and desolate spot and embrace and kiss her., And as last, at some secret meeting, when they are exchanging flowers or betel nut with each other he should take advantage of the occasion and gently caress and touch the secret parts of her body and so bring his love to its desired end.

When a man has made up his mind to seduce a woman he should not try and seduce another at the same time. But, after some time when he has won her and enjoyed her, he can keep the fire of her affection and desire alive by offering her presents, and gradually begin the conquest of another woman.

And if by chance the impatient lover should see the husband of his beloved wandering near the house, he should refrain from having intercourse with the woman even though she may beg him to do so.

Thus a wise man who values his reputation will not think of starting a love affair with a woman who is either timid, fearful, lascivious, frivolous, too well guarded, or who has a mother-and a father-in-law.

CHAPTER 3

A close examination of Women

When a man tries to seduce a woman he should pay particular attention to her mood and humor and act accordingly.

If she listens to his pleas without giving any indications of her feelings or intentions he should then try and win her through the help of a third person.

If she meets him once, and then seeks out an occasion to meet him again and dresses herself with great care on this second occasion, or if she arranges to see him in some solitary place, he may be sure that with a little violence he will be able to take his pleasure.

On the other hand, a woman who lets a man court her for a very long time without ever giving herself to him may be considered a cheat in matters of love. However, knowing the inconstancy of the human spirit, it is possible that one day she may change her mind and if the man has taken care to remain in close contact with her, he may then be able to enjoy her.

If a woman avoids the company of a man and repulses his attention, either through awe of his person or through personal pride, one can, though with difficulty, eventually possess her either by winning her confidence, or by becoming her intimate friend or by using a talented and cunning go-between.

If, however, a man is repulsed by a woman who accompanies her refusal with rash and harmful language he should let the matter drop immediately.

On the other hand, a woman who vehemently refuses a man but at the same time shows him small signs of affection should be taken at all costs.

A woman who meets a man in a lonely place and allows him to touch her with his foot and appears not to notice his gesture—because she is undecided—can be won with patience and perseverance in the following way:

If they should happen to sleep next to each other, he should put his left arm around her and in the morning watch slyly to see if when she awakes, she repulses his gesture seriously or in a way which makes it clear that there is nothing she would like better than to have the caress repeated. And he can repeat the caress with his foot. If after some time she allows him this gesture, he should then try to embrace her even more closely, and if she rises and shrugs off his arm, he must wait and see if she allows him the same opportunity the following day. If indeed she does appear once again and sleeps next to him, he will know that she is not too far from submitting to his pleasure. If, however, she does not reappear, he must try and win her through the intermediary of a clever go-between. If, after some time, she returns and behaves as if nothing had happened between them, he can assume that she has made up her mind and has decided to give herself to him.

When a woman offers a man an opportunity to make known his affection, it is his duty to take advantage of the possibilities the situation offers. The ways in which a woman reveals her desire are simple and can easily be recognized.

She speaks to a man before he has spoken to her;—She arranges to see him in secret places;—She trembles and stammers when she addresses him;—Her fingers and her toes are wet with nervous perspiration and her face is radiant with happiness;—She takes every opportunity to massage his body and to press his head;—While she is massaging she works with only one hand while she lets the other wander over certain parts of his body;—She sits quite still with her hands on his body as if something had surprised her or if she were very tired;—From time to time she bends down to look at her thighs, and if he asks her to allow him to massage them she does not refuse;—She puts one of her hands on his body, and even though the man presses it between his thighs she makes no move to withdraw it;—And lastly, when she has successfully resisted all his efforts to conquer her, she returns the next day and offers to massage his body.

When a woman gives no encouragement to a man, but does not avoid him either, and keeps herself hidden in some solitary place, she can be won through the help of a servant. If when he asks her to come to him she still remains indifferent he should employ the services of a cunning intermediary, but if she still refuses to send him any sign of recognition he should think the matter over carefully before deciding to continue his courtship.

A man should take the initiative in regard to a woman and hold her in deep conversation. He should then allow himself a few amorous advances, and if he feels that she is willing by her response, he should continue without fear until he has achieved his purpose and enjoyed her.

A woman who at the first meeting betrays her attraction and affection by obvious signs can and must very easily be won.

In the same way a lustful woman who responds to amorous hints by immediately showing her willingness for love should be considered as seduced from the beginning of the conversation.

It can perhaps generally be stated that all women, whether wise, simple or trustful, who openly reveal their affection can easily be won.

CHAPTER 4

The Duties of an Intermediary or Go-between

If a woman suggests her interest in a lover by the subtle and unmistakable signs of her body and then suddenly does not allow him to visit her, or very rarely; or if a man wishes to conquer a woman he has only met once, he must employ the services of a go-between.

The go-between must first insinuate herself into the woman's confidence, by fulfilling all her wishes and praising her continually. Then she should try and make her hate or despise her husband, and arouse in her a desire for change and adventure by telling her strange and cunning stories about doctors who are able to make the most sterile woman conceive, news and gossip about her neighbors, and love stories of other men's wives. And she should lavishly praise her beauty, her wisdom, generosity, and goodness.

She should sigh and repeatedly remark: 'It is indeed a shame that a woman such as you, outstanding in every way, should be under the influence of such a husband. Beautiful lady, he is not even worthy to be your servant.'

The go-between should then discuss the small sexual capacity of her husband, his jealousy, vanity, ingratitude, his dislike of pleasure, stupidity, pettiness and any other faults he might possess and which she may happen to know.

She should stress in particular some fault which she knows is particularly irritating to his wife. For instance, if the wife is a doe and the husband is a hare, then there is nothing she can say on that score, but if the wife is a mare or an elephant, then the go-between can take advantage of this sexual disproportion.

Gonikaputra is of the opinion that if the wife is hesitating on the brink of her first love affair, and only reveals the depths of her feelings by timid silences, then her lover should employ a woman she already knows and trusts as a go-between.

When the go-between feels she has successfully managed to sow the seeds of dislike in the wife's breast, she should start to subtly introduce the subject of the lover into the conversation, praise him grandiloquently, and speak of his love and devotion to her, and when she sees the woman's interest and confidence grow, she should tell her the touching story of her suitor.

'A young man of good family has seen you and has fallen

so madly in love with you that he is on the brink of madness. The poor man has such a sensitive nature. He has never before been so shaken by passion and I am afraid that the test might be too much for him, and that he may die of unrequited love.'

If the woman listens attentively to her words, the next day the go-between, noticing signs of interest, should bring up the subject again and talk of the young man and tell her the stories of Ahalya, who was seduced by the king of the Gods, Indra, and of Sakuntala, and Dushyanti, and other such tales that can easily be adapted to the occasion. She should boast of the strength and temperament of the lover, his talents and aptitude in the sixty-four kinds of pleasure listed by Bhabravaya, his health and the love affair he recently had with a noble and aristocratic lady (this last need not necessarily be true).

During all this, the go-between should carefully observe the wife to see if her words have produced any effect. If the wife is interested in the young man, she will sit confidentially next to the go-between and ask detailed questions, such as where she eats, sleeps, and passes her time. Then she will arrange to meet her in little frequented places, and there she will tell her tales, yawn and sigh deeply and longingly, give her presents, talk about some wonderful day they spent together, and leave her hoping to see her again soon, saying with a half-angry air, 'Oh, you are a very clever and eloquent woman, why did you whisper these wicked words to me?' Then she will add that it would be a sin to have a relationship with the young man in question, and she will say nothing of any meetings or conversations she may already have had with him, in the hope that the go-between will question her on the subject and, when she does, the wife must give no definite answer but make light of the man's passion.

When the woman openly reveals her interest and affection, the go-between should start bringing gifts of love from the young man. But if the wife does not know the lover very well, the go-between must soon make them acquainted with each other by praising the lover's qualities and telling exciting stories of his amorous adventures.

Yet Auddalaka is of the opinion that if a man and a woman are not known to each other and have not the opportunity to reveal their interest in each other the service of an intermediary is of no use.

Bhabravaya, on the other hand, asserts that even if the couple have not met, if each one has revealed signs of interest and affection, the services of a go-between can be of great value.

Gonikaputra affirms that a go-between can be employed when two people know each other, even if they have not as yet revealed any signs of affection.

Vatsyayana contests, however, that even if the two concerned have not met, and have shown no signs of affection for each other, they can confide their feelings to a go-between.

The go-between should show the woman the gifts such as flowers, 'pan,' perfumes, and rings that the lover has given her to present to his beloved, and these gifts should bear the marks of the lover's teeth and nails. If he sends her some cloth, he should draw two joined hands on the material to symbolize his ardent prayer. The go-between will also show the woman ornamental figures cut out of leaves, as well as earrings and garlands of flowers, which conceal letters expressing the young man's ardent desire . . . and she should encourage the wife into sending equally symbolic gifts in return.

Once these gifts have been exchanged the go-between should use her own initiative and arrange a rendezvous.

Bhabravaya and his disciples claim that the first meeting should take place during the season when people visit the temples, or at a fair, garden party, theatrical representation, marriage, sacrifice, festival, funeral, or when a group of people go bathing in the river, or during a natural catastrophe, or when brigands attack the town or an enemy invades the country.

Gonikaputra, on the other hand, states that this first rendezvous should be held at the house of women, friends, beggars, astrologers, or ascetics.

But Vatsyayana wisely says that the only convenient place for such a meeting is a place which has an easy entry and exit and where all precautions can be taken to avoid unfortunate incidents, and where the lover can safely leave the house without the risk of meeting someone.

But the task of a go-between is also very varied and there are diverse ways of fulfilling this function:

1) A go-between can accept the whole responsibility of the affair; —2) She can only be involved in a limited way;—3) She may simply carry a letter;—4) She may represent her own desire;— 5) She may represent an innocent young woman;—6) She may be a married woman who acts as a go-between for her husband;— 7) Or a go-between who playes 'the rôle of the wind.'

1) A woman who has observed the mutual affection that binds a certain man and woman, and who brings them together and conducts the whole affair by virtue of her intelligence and cunning, is known as a *go-between who accepts the complete*

responsibility of the affair. This type of go-between is usually employed when the man and the woman already know each other and have had the opportunity of conversing together. In this case she is not only sent by the man (which is the normal procedure in almost all instances where such services are needed) but also by the woman. A go-between who has noticed that a man and a woman are well suited to each other and who tries to bring them together even though they have not as yet met is also known by this same name.

2) A go-between who intervenes in a love affair after the man has already sounded out his beloved and made his feelings known to her is called a *go-between who is involved in a limited way.*

3) A go-between who merely carries messages between a man and a woman who love each other but who are not able to meet or see each other often is a *mere carrier of letters or messages.*

4) A woman who confides to a man that she dreamt that they had intercourse together or who reveals to him that his mistress quarreled with her because she absentmindedly called her by her rival's name, or who gives him gifts bearing marks made by her own fingers and teeth, or shamelessly confesses that she is aware that he has desired her for a long time, and asks him who is more beautiful, his mistress or herself, such a person is known as a *go-between who represents her own desires.* The man should meet and converse with such a woman alone and in secret.

This name is also given to a woman who promises to help a friend seduce the man in question herself by getting to know him and so prevent him from meeting the other woman. The same is true of a man who, never having met the woman, sees her for the first time and then decides to win her for himself and so betrays his friend's confidence.

5) A woman who wins the confidence of the young and innocent wife of a man, and who, without asking her, learns all the secret details of the couple's intimate life and then decides to instruct her in the art of love, teaching her how to express her love, when to be angry and when to be charming; then having made the marks of love—with her own fingers and teeth—on the young woman's body, brings the innocent girl to her husband and excites his passion by showing the love marks on his wife's body is called a *go-between for an innocent wife.* And the husband should reply to his own wife through the same intermediary.

6) When a husband sends his own wife to arouse the interest and desire of a woman he wants to possess, and she goes to her rival and excites her imagination by boasting of her husband's intelligence and prowess, such a wife is called a *married woman who acts as a*

go-between for her husband. The other woman, in such a case, should not hesitate to reply to the man's propositions through the intermediary of his own wife.

7) When a man sends a servant or a young girl to a woman he desires on some pretext or other, and hides a letter in her bouquet of flowers or in her earrings, or makes some significant marks on her body with his fingers or his teeth, this young girl is called a *silent intermediary,* and a man should wait for a reply through the good offices of the same servant.

8) A person who brings a message (with a double meaning) to a woman, which relates to some past love affair, and which is quite unintelligible to the people around her, is called a *go-between who plays the rôle of the wind.* In such a case the answer must also be brought back in the same subtle manner.

A woman astrologer, a servant, a beggar or an artist is usually experienced in the duties of a go-between, and is very easily able to gain the confidence of other women. Each one of them is able, when he so desires, to excite the feelings of interest between two people, praise the friendliness of this or that woman, or describe in detail the sexual arts practiced by another. They can also describe the love a man feels for a certain woman in glowing terms, paint an exciting picture of his ability in sexual intercourse, and boast of the thousands of beautiful women who are madly in love with him, and then come to the point and tactfully explain why he was not able to keep his appointment.

In this way, by the subtle art of her conversation, a go-between can bring together a man and a woman even when the woman would normally never dream of having such a man for a lover, nor the man believe it possible to unite with this woman. She can also reconcile a man and a woman who for some reason or other have been separated for a long time.

CHAPTER 5

*The love of persons
in charge of the wives
of others*

The King and his ministers have no access into the homes and lives of ordinary citizens, and, moreover, their way of life is constantly observed, commented, and emulated by the masses, exactly as in the animal world the beasts awaken when the sun rises and return to their lairs to sleep when the sun sets. Therefore people in public life have the added responsibility of never performing a reproachable act in public which could either lower the dignity of their station or earn them blame and censure. But if such an act is necessary and unavoidable then they must use the appropriate channels as described below.

The head of the village, the supervisor appointed by the King, and the village gleaner are permitted to seduce the village women by the simple procedure of asking them to have intercourse.

The officials mentioned above may have intercourse with these poor women while doing some kind of voluntary work, or when storing the harvest in their barns at the entrance of the house, or when sending off objects during the cleaning of a house, or while working in the fields, or when buying cotton, wool, linen, hemp or thread, and in the season during the buying, selling, and exchange of various articles, and during special jobs. In the same way, the cowboys in the pastures seduce women among the green grasses, and the officials who are put in charge of widows and women without any means of support invariably abuse their confidence and find a means of having intercourse with them. The cleverest satiate their desires by wandering through the villages at night. And there are also some villagers who enter into carnal relations with their daughters-in-law, as they are so often left alone with them. Lastly, the watchmen at the market have intercourse with the village women when they come to sell their wares on market day.

1) During the festival of the eighth moon, that is to say, during the height of the moon of the month of Nargashirsha, as also during the moonlight festival of the month of Kattika, and the spring festival of Chaîtra, the women of the towns and the cities generally pay a visit to the Kings' wives in the Royal Palace. As these visitors are usually known to the Kings' wives they are admitted to

their private apartments and they spend the night laughing, talking, playing games and amusing themselves and only leave the following morning. On this occasion a servant of the King, knowing in advance which woman the King desires, will casually accost that woman just as she is about to return home and invite her to visit some of the curiosities of the palace. In fact, she can have mentioned to the woman some months before that when she comes to visit the harem on the night of the festival, she will take her on a tour of the palace to show her some wonderful curiosities. And, indeed, she will show her the nursery where fantastic climbing plants are raised, the little summer house with its jewel encrusted floor, the vinyards, the floating house, the secret passages in the walls, the paintings, the hunting animals, strange machines, the birds, and the cages of lions and tigers. Finally, when they are alone, she will whisper to her of the love the King bears her, and will tempt her with all the advantages such a liaison will bring her, and she will swear to keep her infidelity a secret. If the woman accepts the proposition, she will thank her by presenting her with marvelous gifts worthy of a King and will accompany her halfway home and take leave of her most affectionately.

2) Or, alternatively, the wives of the King having met the husband of the woman the monarch desires, invite the wife to the palace, where a servant of the King is sent in all haste to make a similar proposition.

3) Or, one of the King's wives can become friendly with the woman he wishes to seduce, and sending one of her intimates to her, she can invite her to visit the palace. When she visits the harem the King will send one of his trusted servants to tempt her to have intercourse with him.

4) Similarly, one of the King's wives can invite the woman desired by the King to the palace to take part in some artistic endeavor and then the King can once again dispatch an intermediary.

5) Or a beggar in connivance with one of the King's wives can say to the woman the King desires—and whose husband may have lost his fortune or may be afraid of the King for some reason: 'This wife of the King has a lot of influence over her husband. She is also very kind and welcoming, and we should address ourselves to her in this matter. I shall undertake to smuggle you into the harem and then she will handle the affair so that your husband will have no more reason to fear the King's wrath.' If the woman accepts this offer, the beggar will take her on two or three visits to the harem, and the obliging Queen will promise her that she will intercede with the King on behalf of her husband. The grateful woman, flattered by the Queen's attentions, will return

often to the harem after that, and then one day the King will send his intermediary to make her an offer she dare not refuse.

6) This manner of winning a woman also holds true for the wives of men who desire to work for the King, or who are oppressed by his ministers, or who are poor and not satisfied with their situation in life, or who desire to creep into the King's favor, or become famous among his people, or who are persecuted by members of their own caste, and so wish to prove their worth, or who act as spies for the King or who wish to attain a particular goal.

7) Lastly, if the woman the King desires is living with a man who is not her husband, the King can have her arrested, and reduced to slavery because of her crime, and so place her in his harem.

8) Or the King makes his ambassador seek a quarrel with the husband of the woman he wants, and then he can imprison her as the wife of his enemy and eventually place her in his harem.

These methods of winning the wives of other men are generally practiced by Kings in their palaces. But the King should never enter the dwelling of an ordinary person. For Abhira, King of the Kottas, was killed by a washerman when he was in a stranger's house, and Jayasana, King of the Kashis, was massacred by mistake, in similar circumstances, by his own knights.

But, depending on the customs in different lands, Kings sometimes have special facilities for making love to the wives of other men. Thus in the land of the Andras, newly-wed brides traditionally present themselves on the tenth day of the wedding to offer gifts to the King at the palace. Then after he has enjoyed them, they are dismissed. In the land of the Vatsagulmas, the wives of the Prime Ministers offer themselves to the King in the evenings.

In the province of the Vaidharbas, the wives of the natives spend one month in the Royal harem pretending that they do so out of love for his person.

The Aparatakas send their most beautiful women as gifts to the King and his ministers.

And lastly, in the land of the Saurashtras the town and village women go to the Royal Palace for the King's pleasure, either in groups or separately.

These methods cited here
Are often used by Kings
To capture the hearts of his people's wives;
But a monarch who loves his subjects

And wishes to see them prosper
Never indulges in such deceits;
For a King who has conquered the six enemies of humanity—
Becomes a master of the world.

CHAPTER 6

The women of the Royal harem
and the protection of one's own
wife

The women of the Royal harem are so strictly guarded that they never see or meet a man; but their desires are never satisfied, as their husband has to divide his time among so many women. And it is because of this that they indulge in many strange sorts of pleasure.

They sometimes dress their servants, confidantes or friends in men's clothing and soothe their desires by inserting a fruit, root or bulb that has the form of a lingam; or they lie on a statue that possesses a lingam in erection.

Certain Kings are concerned enough about their wives' problems to drug themselves nightly so that they may enjoy several women every day, though normally they may not feel like it, nor possess the physical endurance for such a feat; others only have intercourse with those wives they love; while some make love to a different wife each night, so that every wife has her turn.

However, with the help of their servants the King's wives sometimes receive men in the harem, disguised as women. The confidantes and servants who are aware of all the secrets of the palace try to tempt young men to take the risk of entering the harem by telling them of the good fortune that awaits them there and assuring them that there is no danger involved as the access and exit is easy, as the guards are very negligent, and most of them are sympathetic and turn a blind eye when it concerns the Queens. But these women should never force a young man to enter by tempting him with lies, for such an action could mean his doom.

As to the young man himself, he would do much better to renounce any such enterprise because of the risks and dangers involved.

If, however, he wishes to undertake this hazardous adventure, he should first make sure that there is an easy exit, that the palace is encircled by a garden, and if there is a door which leads out into this garden, if the guards are easy-going and if the King is really absent, and then when the women of the harem signal to him to enter, he should first look carefully around to see if the coast is clear and then slip in by the secret door they show him. If it is at all possible he should wander casually around the palace some days before, and invent some pretext to chat with the guards and servants. He can even confide his desires to the latter. Lastly, he should leave the task of a go-between to some woman who has regular access to the harem and he should learn to recognize the emissaries of the King.

If there is no go-between who has access to the harem the man should hide in a place from where he can see the woman he loves and desires to possess.

If the place is well guarded he should disguise himself as a servant of the desired Queen. When she looks at him he should reveal his sentiments to her by signs and gestures, show her suggestive pictures and objects, and give her garlands of flowers and rings. He should carefully observe her reactions and answers which she will also communicate to him by signs and gestures, and then he should try and enter the harem. If he knows for certain that she is to come to a certain place, he should hide until the moment of her arrival and then enter in the bustle along with her guards. He can also enter by hiding in a folding bed or in a carpet, but the best method of all is to make himself invisible by means of an ointment which he applies to his body. Here is the recipe:

Burn together, without allowing the smoke to escape, the heart of an ichneumon, the fruit of the tumbi, and the eyes of a snake. Grind the ashes and mix them with an equal quantity of water. Then apply this mixture on the eyes, and a man can go anywhere without being seen.

There are also other ways of rendering oneself invisible, prescribed by the Brahmins of Duyana and the Jogashiras.

A man can also slip into the harem during the festival of the eighth moon in the month of Naggastirsha, during the moonlight festivals when the palace guards are distracted and occupied by the feasting and merrymaking.

Entry into the harem is easiest when some object is being taken in or out of the palace, or during drinking feasts when the guards are very busy, or when one of the Royal brides changes her residence, or when the Queens go to the public gardens or to a fair, and when they return in a large group, or when the King is away on a long pilgrimage. The wives in the harem all know each other's secrets and, as they all have the same aim, they help each other very willingly. A young man who pleases all the wives can continue his pleasant task for as long as the affair rests secret and no whisper or gossip finds its way outside the harem.

The wives of the King of the Aparatakas are very badly guarded and many young men enter the harem through the intermediary of women who have free access to the harem.

The women of the King of Ahira console themselves with the sentinels of the harem, who are known as kshtriyas.

The Queens of Vatsagulmas arrange to have their lovers enter along with their messengers and servants.

In Vaidarbhas the sons of the Queens enter the harem freely and enjoy the women there, with the exception of their mothers.

In Stri-rajya the women of the King give themselves to their caste members and their relatives.

In Ganda the Queens enjoy Brahmins, their friends, their servants and their slaves.

In Samdhava the servants, stepbrothers and other close associates enjoy the women of the harem.

In the land of the Himavatas courageous citizens bribe the guards and enter the harem.

In the land of the Vanyas and the Kalmyas the Brahmins employed by the King enter the harem, ostensibly to offer flowers to the Queens, and take advantage of their privilege to talk with them privately behind a curtain and eventually end by possessing them completely.

Lastly, the wives of the King of the Prachyas hide a young man for every ten women of the harem.

It is for these reasons that every husband should guard his wife well.

The ancient writers claim that a King should choose men noted for their indifference to carnal matters as guards over the harem. On the other hand, these same people, though impervious to temptation, could through fear or greed allow other men to penetrate into the harem, which leads Gonikaputra to write that a King must employ as guards men free from carnal desire, greed and fear. Moreover, care should be taken to see that the guards are not intimidated by fear of Dharma into allowing Brahmins and other such persons to enter the women's quarters.

The disciples of Bhabravaya say that a husband should encourage his wife to be confiding in any woman who will later tell him all the secrets and gossip of the neighborhood and so will also inform him of the truth concerning his wife's chastity.

But Vatsyayana states that wicked men always succeed with women and a husband should not expose his innocent wife to the corrupting influence of a gossip and a traitor.

The chastity of a woman is often endangered because of the following reasons:

Frequent visits to parties and social gatherings;—Lack of reserve; —Debauchery of the husband;—A lack of prudence in her relations with other men;—Frequent and prolonged absence of her husband;—Long visits to foreign lands;—The destruction of her love and finer sensibilities by her husband;—The company of dissolute women;—Jealousy of the husband.

A man who has learned the art of seduction in the Shastras
Is never betrayed by his own wives.
But he should never seduce the wives of others
Because a virtuous woman's refusal may hurt his pride
And cause him to lose the merits of Artha and Dharma.
This book, whose object is the art of life,
Tries to teach men to please and cherish their own wives
And this volume should not be used as a guide
To the forbidden bed of another's companion.

PART SIX

COURTESANS AND PROSTITUTES

CHAPTER 1

Why courtesans seek men; the ways of attracting a
desired person, and the types of men with whom it is
advisable to have a relationship

Men provide courtesans with two satisfactions: sexual fulfillment
and pleasure, and the means of earning a livelihood.

When a courtesan proposes to give herself to a man she loves,
this action is natural; but when she submits to him only to earn
money the action is forced and artificial. However, even in the
second circumstance she should behave as if she loved him, because men prefer women who are devoted and attentive to them.
The wise courtesans make their lovers believe that money is un-
important to them, and it is a good investment for the future if at
the beginning of a liaison she desists from extorting money from
her protector by tricks and guile.

To attract the attention of passing men, the courtesan should
dress herself in her most beautiful robes, wear all her ornaments
and stand or sit in the doorway of her house. Without being too
obvious, she should from time to time look into the street so that
passers-by may study her face, for after all, she is in a sense an
object for sale. She should choose her friends amongst people who
can help her to meet clients, and who are capable of causing difficulties between rich men and their mistresses, so that she may
profit from the quarrel. She should cultivate these friends, for they
can help her when she is in difficulties, help her to earn money,
and protect her from the insults and brutal revenge of slighted
lovers. The people who can best fulfill this rôle are:

The civic guard of the police;—Officers attached to the Court of
Justice;—Astrologers;—Poor men who feel they can better their

circumstances;—Intellectuals;—Teachers and exponents of the sixty-four arts;—The Pithamardas or confidantes;—The Vitas or parasites of society;—Flower merchants;—Perfumers;—Wine sellers;—Laundrymen;—Barbers;—Beggars.

On the other hand, the courtesan can best practice her trade among men who are pleasure-loving, vain, rich, young, or powerful, such as:

Men with an independent income;—Young men;—Those who are completely unattached;—Governors under the King;—Men who earn a good living without much effort;—Those who possess a certain source of revenue, such as landowners, etc.;—Men who believe themselves to be handsome;—Men who love to boast;—A eunuch who wishes to pass for a man;—A man who hates his equals;—A naturally liberal and broadminded person;—A man who has some influence with the King or with one of his ministers;—A man who is always happy;—A man who is proud of his fortune;—A man who disobeys the orders of his elders;—A man who is under the surveillance of members of his own caste;—The only son of a rich father;—An ascetic who is profoundly troubled by carnal desire;—A brave man;—The King's physician;—Old acquaintances.

She should also try and cultivate men of excellent qualities for the good of her reputation, and perhaps also because she personally loves and admires such men. The men who win the love and admiration of such women are:

Well-born men who know the world and do the right thing at the right time;—Poets;—A good story-teller;—Eloquent men;—Men who are active and talented in the arts;—Men of foresight;—Men who possess the virtue of firm devotion, and are liberal, even-tempered and affectionate to their parents;—Those who love society;—Those who can complete the verses begun by another;—Those who possess a knowledge of different sports;—Men who are free from illnesses and diseases, who possess a well-proportioned body, and a good and robust constitution;—Men not given to alcoholism;—Men indefatigable in matters of love;—Men who love women and attract their love reciprocally without ever becoming their slaves;—Men with independent incomes;—Men free from envy and jealousy;—Men having a trustful and unsuspicious nature.

The courtesan, on the other hand, should possess the following qualities:

She should be beautiful, kind, and possess signs of good omen on her body. She should appreciate the good qualities of others and love luxury and riches. She should delight in having sexual intercourse with a man she loves, be firm and determined and take care to see that she belongs to the same sexual category as the man.

She must always keep an open mind and show her willingness to acquire new experiences and knowledge. She must not be miserly and always be eager to join in social gatherings and artistic circles.

In fact, she can sum up the ideal qualities of the female sex: intelligent, well-mannered, dependable, grateful and appreciative; cautious and foresighted; energetic; of good conduct; aware of the right time and the right place to perform certain acts or ask for favors; polite in manner and speech, with no traces of vulgarity, malice, or anger. Furthermore, she must not be stupid, avaricious, and she should have a profound knowledge of the Kama Shatras, as well as a talent for the arts connected with this work.

The absence of one or many of these qualities result in the defects common to women.

The courtesan should, however, avoid the following categories of men:

A consumptive;—One of a sickly mental or moral disposition;— One who always has an appropriate verse ready for the occasion; —One whose breath smells like human excreta;—One who loves his wife;—One who uses brutal language;—A man who is always suspicious;—A miser;—A man without mercy;—A thief;—An idiot; —A man who is fascinated by magical experiments;—One who does not care about his reputation;—A man who can be corrupted even by the money of his enemies;—A man who is exaggerately puritanical and prudish.

The ancient writers are of the opinion that when a courtesan propositions a man she is guided by one of the following motives: love;—fear;—money;—pleasure;—some revenge she wishes to fulfill;—curiosity;—sorrow;—habit;—Dharma;—desire for fame;—compassion;—desire to have a friend;—shame;—the striking resemblance of the man to a loved one;—search of happiness;—desire to break relations with her present lover;—a similar physical category as the man;—cohabitation;—constancy and poverty.

But Vatsyayana believes that desire for wealth, comfort and love are the main principles which motivate a courtesan to give herself to a man.

Now a courtesan should never sacrifice money or the possibility of earning money for love, as money is the principal motivation of her life. But if she is afraid of someone or something, then it is quite acceptable to choose a lover for his physical strength who will be able to protect her from harm.

Moreover, even if a man asks her to come to his home for the sole purpose of indulging in sexual diversion, she should not instantly accept, for men are apt to despise everything which is easily possessed or won. She should first send masseurs, singers or clowns that she may employ, or the Pithamardas or a confidante to investigate the exact nature of the man's sentiments towards her. Through these intermediaries she will know whether the man is pure or impure, whether he is well disposed, capable of affection, indifferent, liberal or miserly; and if after considering all the factors she finds him to her taste, she should engage the Vitas or other such persons to bring them together.

Thus, after having studied the situation, the courtesan should ask the Pithamarda to lead the aspiring lover to her house on some pretext, such as to watch a cock fight, or a combat of rams, or partridges; or to hear the Maina bird talk, or watch a play or participate in some artistic endeavor; or he can lead the courtesan to the man's house.

When the prospective lover comes to her house, the courtesan should make a gift to him of some object destined to arouse his curiosity and to excite his desire, such as an instrument that is closely connected with intercourse, and she should coyly tell him that it is especially intended for his use. She must amuse him all evening, telling him interesting stories and performing certain actions that she knows will please him. When he leaves, she will send one of her servants capable of holding a clever and double-edged conversation to him frequently and will also make him small gifts from time to time. Sometimes she will go to visit him herself, pretending she needs his advice, but she should always be accompanied by a Pithamarda.

Garlands of flowers, incense, perfumed and spiced 'pan'
Are the means by which a courtesan welcomes her lover;
And while she binds her spell with words
Her body should whisper secrets of its proficiency in the art of love.
She must give him strange gifts, exchange subtle gages of mutual
[desire;
But always her body must whisper its challenge to love;
And when the first close clasp of love is over
The subtle courtesan can keep her lover's devotion
By her agreeable nature, friendly spirit and magic words,
But above all, by a thousand diversions on the road to love.

CHAPTER 2

Temporary Marriage of Courtesans

When a servant reaches the age of puberty, her master should confine her, and when as a result of her seclusion and the difficulty of approaching her, her suitors desire her with ever increased ardor, he should give her to the one who can promise her the most riches and happiness.

This is one of the ways of heightening one's value in another's eyes.

In the same way, when the daughter of a courtesan arrives at the age of menstruation, the mother should gather several young men of the same age, disposition and intellect as her daughter, and announce that she will give her child in marriage to the one that can promise her or give her certain gifts.

Afterwards the girl should be hidden away, and the mother should give her in marriage to the man who is ready to make her these gifts. If the mother cannot obtain everything she desires from the young man she should produce some ornament—that in reality belongs to her—and pretend that it was given to her daughter by her fiancé.

Or again her mother can allow her daughter to marry the man privately, as if she did not know anything about it, and then when she 'finds out' she can give her consent to the union.

The girl should also make herself attractive to the sons of rich citizens, and unknown to her mother she should secretly meet them during music and singing lessons or when she goes with a group of friends for a musical evening in a stranger's house, and then she should beg her mother through the intermediary of a servant or friends to allow her to unite with the man of her choice.

When the daughter of a courtesan is given to a man in this way she must observe the rules of marriage during one year and after that she is free to do as she pleases. But even after this year if her first husband invites her to come and visit him from time to time she must give up any other engagement no matter how profitable and go to him.

This is the style of temporary marriage common to courtesans and also the way in which they increase their attractions. The same is true of young dancers, whose mothers should only give them to men who can be of some use to them in life.

CHAPTER 3

On the Courtesan who lives as a 'Wife' with a man

When a courtesan decides to live with a man as if she were his wife, she must be chaste and faithful and satisfy him in every way. In other words, her duty must be to please him both physically and spiritually, but she must never become truly attached to him, even though she may pretend to be entirely devoted to him alone.

To make this doubly difficult task easier she should resort to certain ruses. She can say that she has a mother who is a very bitter and avaricious woman and is solely preoccupied with the idea of earning money. If she has no mother she must ask an old nurse or a confidante to assume this rôle. Then, the older woman should pretend to disapprove of the lover and try to force the courtesan to leave him. She, on the other hand, must pretend to be torn between the two, and she should be alternatively angry, downtrodden, fearful and ashamed. But under no circumstances should she disobey her mother or nurse. If she wishes to visit her lover she should lie to her guardian and tell her that he is very ill and that she must visit him, and so slip away to spend an evening in delight.

Here are the ways a young courtesan can secure the love and respect of her lover.

She should send her servant to gather the flowers that he wore the night before and has discarded. Then she should wear these same old flowers as a sign of her affection for him.

She must also beg him for the 'pan' he has not eaten and was thinking of throwing away.

She will express her surprise and admiration for the method of love-making he has just shown her, and she should always show her respect for his adroitness in love.

She will learn the sixty-four arts of pleasure, as enumerated by Bhabravaya, from him and will always make love to him in the way he likes and has taught her. She must keep his secrets and confide her secret desires and wishes to him, and never show her anger.

Whenever he looks in her direction, she must never omit to gently address an intimate part of his body in reply; she must kiss his body all over when he is asleep, look at him anxiously when he is pensive or worried or thinks of something other than herself, and she must never demonstrate unseemly pleasure or too artificially feigned coldness when she sees him in the street.

She should hate his enemies, love those who are dear to him, be gay or sad in accordance with his mood; express the desire to see his other women, and suspect that the marks and bites she has made on his body were made by other women; she must not express her love for him in words, but by acts, signs and half-hinted phrases.

The perfect courtesan must remain silent when her lover sleeps, lies drunk or ill, and she must listen attentively to his own accounts of his good works and never neglect to remind him of his generous actions.

She should joke with him and reply wittily to his questions when she sees that their relations are familiar enough to allow for such liberties. She should listen to all his stories except those which concern her rivals or his other conquests, and she should express concern and chagrin if he yawns, sighs or faints in her company.

If he sneezes she must instantly wish him a long life, and she shall pretend to be ill or desire to become pregnant when she feels bored. She shall never praise any other man and will also never criticize anyone who possesses the same defects as her lover.

She will always wear any ornaments he may have given her, but must avoid wearing the same clothes too often.

When he is ill, she will not eat, but sit beside him, consoling him and sharing his suffering. And she shall insist on accompanying him if he leaves the country of his own accord or if he is banished by the King. She must constantly tell him that if she is to be separated from him she does not wish to live, and that the unique object and aim of her life is to be united to him.

She must offer sacrifices—that she has promised beforehand—to the Gods when he acquires riches or obtains his desires, or when he has just recovered from some illness or indisposition.

The courtesan should never be too familiar with her lover, yet she should cleverly mingle his name and that of her family in the songs she sings. She should place his hand on her thighs, breast and forehead, and should close her eyes and express her ecstasy at feeling his hands on her body, then she should sit on his knees and go to sleep with her head on his shoulders just like a child.

She must desire to have his child, never reveal his secrets and dissuade him from undertaking fasts and abstinences, saying: 'Let me bear the burden of the sin,' and she must share his fasts and his religious sacrifices when she sees that it is impossible to change his mind, and she should always flatter him by telling him that his fasts and religious observances are difficult to observe even for her.

She must look after his wealth and person without any distinctions; never appear at social gatherings without him and she must accompany him everywhere if he so desires it. She should be delighted to wear things discarded by him and to eat the food he has left over. But, above all, she should respect his family, character, ability in the arts, caste, color, good, qualities, charm, friends, and his native land.

She should encourage him to sing or demonstrate any talents that he may have, and go to meet him without any regard for the heat, cold, rain or storm. And she should assure him that even in the next world she will be his mistress.

The perfect mistress should regulate her life in accordance with her lover's tastes and habits. She should never indulge in sorcery. If her mother tries to restrain her and limit her visits to her lover or attempts to wrest her away from him by force, she should fight with her, threaten to kill herself with some sharp instrument, hang herself or go on a hunger strike.

Lastly through the good offices of her friends she should take every opportunity to assure her lover of the depth and constancy of her affections, and even though she receives money for it, she should never discuss her affairs with her mother.

If her lover goes on a journey, she must beg him to return as soon as possible, and during his absence she should not neglect her religious duties and only wear ornaments that bring good luck. If, however, he does not return on the expected day, she should try and divine the date of return through certain presages, news gathered from her neighbors, and the position of the planets, moon and stars. During a game, or if she receives a sign of good augur she should say: 'I wish we were soon reunited.' And if she feels unhappy or sees an unlucky omen she should instantly perform a propitiatory ceremony to the Gods.

When her lover returns she should thank the God Kama and also perform thanksgiving ceremonies to the other Gods. Then she must ask her friends to bring her an urn of water, and she should honor the crow that eats the offerings placed before the relics of the dead ancestors. After their first reunion she should ask her lover to perform certain devotional rites along with her, which he will certainly do if he is at all attached to her.

It is said that a man is deeply attached to a woman if his love is disinterested, if he shares the same objectives as his beloved, when he has complete confidence in her, and when he does not think of her in terms of money.

The dimensions of women's love are fathomless;
Even the beloved cannot sound its depths:
For the subtleness, delicacy and natural restraint

Veils the image of love in mystery.
Women can never be seen in the light of their true nature,
Whether they love or are indifferent.
Whether they satisfy or turn away in distaste
Nor even when they succeed in grasping all the fortune a man
[possesses.

CHAPTER 4

The best ways to earn money. The signs which indicate that a lover is losing interest and the way to break a relationship

Money can be obtained from a lover in two ways: by natural and legal means, or by tricks and guile.

The ancient sages point out that if a courtesan can obtain as much money from her lover as she needs, she should not resort to guile. But Vatsyayana wisely points out that if she can obtain as much money as she needs through perfectly legal means, and if she knows that if she uses guile she can get double the amount, then she will in any case use all the tricks she knows to get as much as possible.

There are many tricks a courtesan can utilize to obtain money from a lover:

She can ask him for money on various occasions, to buy certain articles such as ornaments, food, drink, flowers, perfumes and clothes, while in reality she will not buy anything or buy these articles much cheaper and so put some money away.

She can praise his intelligence.

She can pretend she has to buy gifts to distribute on certain festival days.

Or she can tell him that in leaving her house, her jewels were stolen or seized by the King's Guard.

She can weep and tell him that her property has been destroyed by fire, or has collapsed through the negligence of her servants.

She can pretend to have lost the ornaments belonging to her lovers, along with her own.

Friends of her lover, at her instigation, should tell him of the high expenses she incurs every time she comes to visit him.

She can owe money in her lover's name.

She can arrange to quarrel with her mother about some money she has spent on her lover, despite her mother's protestations.

She can refuse to attend parties or feasts given by friends because she is ashamed as she has no money to buy them gifts, having previously informed her lover of the rich presents she has received from these same people.

She will not perform certain religious ceremonies, claiming that she has not enough money to undertake such expense.

She should hire dancers and musicians to amuse her lover.

She can ask for money to entertain ministers in a befitting way, as well as doctors, saying she needs their help.

She can state that she needs money to help her friends or benefactors who have fallen on evil times.

She can claim that she must observe all the ceremonies of the Domestic Gods.

She can protest to have paid for the marriage of a friend who has no family.

She can insist that she must satisfy her cravings while she is pregnant.

She can claim to be ill and double the doctor's bill for her treatment.

She can say that she has to help a friend out of a difficult situation.

She can say that she is going to sell some of her jewels to buy a present for her lover.

She can pretend to have sold some of her ornaments, furniture and household goods to a merchant, who is aware of the rôle he has to play.

She can say that she must buy a very much more expensive set of kitchen utensils so that these can be easily distinguished from others, and it will not be easy for a dishonest servant to change them for others of an inferior quality.

She will remind her lover of the first liberties he took with her, and will have him continually reminded of these early days by her friends and followers.

She will boast to him of the large amounts of money earned by other courtesans.

She will speak of her own earnings before these other courtesans and before her lover and boast that she earns twice as much as any of them, even though this may not be true.

She will loudly and openly oppose her mother who must urge

her to accept some former lovers because of the money they are willing to give her.

She will subtly tell her lover about the generosity of his rivals.

A woman should always carefully observe the subtle changes in the behavior of her lover, for often these changes indicate that his sentiments and feelings as regards her have similarly changed.

For instance, a man who has ceased to love his mistress and is thinking of breaking the liaison behaves in the following ways:

1) He gives his mistress just enough money to satisfy her most basic needs, or sometimes he purposely gives her something other than what she has asked him for;—2) He keeps her constantly in a state of uncertainty about his various promises;—3) He changes his plans and projects continuously;—4) He does not satisfy her desires, either sexual or material;—5) He forgets his promises, or does quite the opposite of what he has promised;—6) He has mysterious whispered conversations with his domestics;—7) He often spends the night in another house, saying that he has to see a friend about something important;—8) He is often seen in conversation with the followers of another courtesan he used to know a long time ago.

When a courtesan notices the subtle changes that come over her lover, she should quickly deposit all the jewels and presents her lover gave her in a safe place, before he discovers her intention and tries to take back his gifts with the help of a bailiff he knows, as the payment for debts she has incurred in his name. Then if the lover is rich and has always been kind and generous to her, she should continue to treat him with respect. But if he is poor, she should get rid of him quickly and ignore him completely in the future.

There are many ways of dismissing a lover:

The courtesan can accuse her lover of leading a disagreeable and odious life and laugh scornfully at his vices and eccentricities;—She will constantly talk about an affair that he knows nothing about;—She will show no admiration for his knowledge, but on the contrary will criticize him and his ideas;—She will try and humiliate him;—She will prefer the company of men who are wiser and more accomplished than he;—She will not miss an opportunity to show her scorn for him;—She will criticize other men who have the same faults as he;—She will show her distaste for his methods of lovemaking;—She will refuse him her mouth;—She will not allow him to caress her stomach, waist or thighs;—She will respond with nothing but disgust to the bites and scratches he lovingly inflicts on her;—She will not press herself against him when he embraces her;—She will lie immobile and unresponsive during the act of love;—She will laugh at his love for her;—She will never return his caresses or kisses and pretend to be sleepy when he desires to have intercourse with her;—When he wishes to spend the day with her, she will plead a previous engagement and go out to visit a friend;—She must pretend to find it difficult to understand him, and laugh suddenly without any good reason. And when he tells a joke, she should listen distractedly and then laugh about something completely different;—She will exchange sly glances with her servants and clap her hands when he wishes to speak to them;—She will interrupt him in the middle of a story and begin to tell a completely different one herself;—She should tell everyone about his defects and vices and declare them incorrigible;—She will also tell her servants things that she knows will hurt his pride;—She must never look up to greet him when he comes to see her;—Always she will ask him for things she knows he cannot give her.

Finally she will dismiss him.

The life and aim of a courtesan:

She must entice men of good standing, and after a careful examination of their means start a liaison. She must be true and affectionate to the man she lives with, and obtain as much money as possible from the man who loves her and then send him away after she has taken everything from him.

A courtesan who lives with one man as if she were married to him does not have the encumbrance of many importunate lovers, and still gains as much wealth and riches as she desires.

CHAPTER 5

On beginning a new relationship with a former lover

When a courtesan abandons a lover after having enjoyed his wealth and led him on the path to ruin, she should start to think of beginning a new affair with an old lover.

But she should not try to renew the old friendship unless she is sure that he has become rich, or that he still has a lot of wealth or that he is still fond of her. And if this man happens to be living with another woman at the time, she should think the matter over carefully before making any decision.

Now a former lover can be involved in one of the following six situations:

1) He can have left the first mistress of his own will and even have left another since then;—2) He can have been rejected by the two women;—3) He can have left one woman of his own volition but have been sent away by the other;—4) He may have left a woman of his own choice and be living with another at present;— 5) He could have been sent away by one woman and left the second of his own will;—6) He can have been sent away by one woman and at present be living with another.

1) Now if this man has left two women, it is not worth the trouble to try and renew the old friendship, as he is obviously an unstable personality and was completely oblivious to the good qualities of his two mistresses.

2) If the man was sent away by the second mistress because she saw an opportunity of making more money out of another man, then it is worthwhile to rekindle the old flame as, if he is still attached to the first woman, he will give her much more money, because his pride has been wounded and he wishes to spite the other woman. But if he was sent away because of his poverty or miserly nature, then there is no use in seeking him out.

3) In the case of a man who deserted the first mistress and was sent away by the second, if he consents to return to the first and gives her lots of money, it is worth welcoming him back.

4) If a man left his first love and is now living with another woman, and the first mistress wishes to have him back, she should first try and find out why he left her. If he left her because he expected to find in the second mistress certain qualities that the first one lacked, and if he has been disappointed, and is at present disposed to return to his former lover and to give her lots of money as a sign of his repentance and because he still is fond of her, the first mistress should accept such an offer. Or perhaps he has discovered so many defects in the second woman that he has exaggerated the qualities possessed by the first, and is at present ready to give her anything because he feels she is unexcelled.

But before renewing such a relationship, the courtesan should carefully estimate if he is a weak man, or one who likes to possess many women, or who loves a poor woman, or who has never done anything for the women he lives with. Only after she has considered all these factors should she make her decision.

5) As to the man who was sent away by one woman and voluntarily left the other, if the first mistress wishes to take him back she should first make sure that he still has some regard for her and if he is willing to spend a lot of money on her. For though he

appreciates her good qualities he may still prefer another woman; or if she sent him away before he satisfied his sexual desires, he may return to her only to avenge the insult; or if he desires to return also to seize hold of the money she once took from him, win it back, and so ruin her. Or he may just want to make her break with her present lover and then refuse her himself and so leave her stranded and unprotected.

If after having carefully examined all these possibilities she believes him to be true and honest in his intentions she should take him back. But if she in any way suspects or distrusts him, she should refuse to have any relations with him.

6) If, however, the former lover was sent away by his first love and is now living with another woman, and if he shows his desire to return to the one who spurned him, the courtesan ought to think the matter over thoroughly before accepting, and while the present mistress is doing everything to keep him, the first should do everything she can—behind the scenes of course—to recapture his heart. She should reason with herself in the following manner:

a) I sent him away unjustly and without any good reason and now he has been forced to go to another woman. Therefore I ought to do my best to win him back.

b) If only he speaks to me once—he will certainly leave the other woman.

c) Thanks to my former lover, I shall be able to humiliate the one I have at present.

d) He has become rich, acquired a good position and fulfills some important official functions for the King.

e) He is separated from his wife.

f) He has become independent.

g) He lives away from his father or brother.

h) In seducing him once again I shall gain a very rich lover, that only my present man prevents me from having.

i) As his wife does not respect him any more I can successfully separate them.

j) The friend of this man loves my rival who detests me. It would give me an an opportunity of breaking up my rival's love affair.

k) And lastly I shall discredit him if I recapture his love, for it will demonstrate the instability of his nature.

Once a courtesan has made up her mind to recapture a former lover's affection, her Pithamarda, or some other servants, must tell him that she had previously sent him away only on the instigation of her mother; that in reality she loves him as passionately as she did the first day, but that she obeyed her mother's command out of deference and respect. They must also tell him that she is miserable with her present lover whom she detests with all her heart, and they must try and restore his confidence in her by reminding him of his former passion for her, and they should nostalgically tell him about a certain love-bite he gave her that she has never, never forgotten. This allusion to the love-bite will arouse certain memories, such as the particular way he used to kiss, or the way they used to have intercourse together.

When a woman has the choice of taking a stranger as a new lover or returning to a former love, the Acharyas (wise men) are of the opinion that the latter is preferable, as the woman knows the tastes and habits of her former lover and so will be better able to please and satisfy him.

But Vatsyayana believes that a former lover who has already spent a great deal of his wealth on this woman will not be able or will not want to spend much more, and so he will be less reliable than a stranger who may be passionately in love with her. However, there are of course exceptions to this general rule, and everything depends on the personality of the man.

A new love with a former lover can be desirable
If it separates a certain woman from a certain man,
Or if by jealousy it produces a good effect on the present lover.
When a man is blinded by passion
He becomes afraid of others;
And to preserve his burning love
He closes his desire-filled eyes
To all faults and defects of the beloved,
And buys her love with gifts of money.
A courtesan must be kind and considerate
And faithful to the man that loves her
And refuse the one that scorns and dishonors her.
But, if one day, the latter sends a messenger
She may refuse to see him, or make a secret tryst,
But she should never leave the man with whom she lives
And who loves and shelters her from want and sorrow.
A wise woman before she pours her love into ancient mold
Should make sure that this old union full of memories
Will bring her happiness, riches, love and friendship.

CHAPTER 6

Different sorts of Gain

If a courtesan can each day earn a lot of money because she has a large clientele she should not attach herself to one man. She should fix her price for one night, taking into consideration the time, the place, the season, the resources of her customers, her own physical appearance, disposition and qualities, and she should regulate these prices with those being charged by other courtesans. She should inform her lovers, friends, and acquaintances of her prices, but if she has the opportunity of acquiring wealth from one lover, then she should give herself to him alone and live with him as if she were his wife.

Now the Sages are of the opinion that if a courtesan has a choice between two lovers of equal wealth and generosity she should choose the one who will give her precisely the thing she most desires.

Vatsyayana believes that the woman should accept that man who gives her gold, as gold cannot be so easily taken back as some other objects, and it is a means of acquiring all the things one desires. Of all such articles, like silver, brass, metal, iron, vases, furniture, beds, clothes and undergarments, perfumes and ointment, vessels made out of gourds, oil, wheat, cattle, etc. the most valuable is gold.

If the conquest of the two lovers entails the same effort and one wishes to obtain the same thing from either one, then one should ask an objective friend to choose between the two; or one can decide on the merit of their personal qualities, or on the basis of the good and bad portents and birthmarks they have on their bodies.

If there are two lovers, and one is deeply in love with the courtesan while the other is simply generous, the Sages claim that the woman should choose the generous one. But Vatsyayana believes that it is better to choose the one that is devoted to the courtesan, as he may later become generous, and it is certain that even a miser gives money to the woman he loves, while an overly generous man never becomes deeply attached. But, if among her suitors who truly love her, there is a poor and a rich man, she must of course choose the rich man.

If there are two lovers and one is generous and the other is always ready to be of service, some Sages feel it is wiser to choose the latter, but Vatsyayana points out that a man who does a favor feels that he has done his duty once and for all, while a generous man never thinks of the money he gives. Here again the courtesan should decide on the basis of which one of the two will give her greater benefits in the long run.

If one of the lovers is grateful and the other liberal, certain Sages claim that the courtesan should prefer the liberal one. But Vatsyayana is of the opinion that she should choose the first, because liberal men are usually high-handed, and rough without much regard for others. These so-called liberal men do not think twice about the matter if they discover some defect in the character of the courtesan, or, if some woman says evil things about her, they break up the liaison right away without even thinking of past services she has rendered them. The grateful man, on the other hand, will never suddenly let her down, for he will be appreciative of the trouble she has always taken to please him. But here again the courtesan should be guided in her choice by future possibilities.

When a courtesan finds herself faced with the choice of complying with the request of a friend or of earning money, the Sages say she should concentrate on earning money. But Vatsyayana disagrees and remarks that money can be found as well tomorrow as today, but if one neglects the request of a friend he can bear her a grudge for life.

In the same way the courtesan can tell her friend that she is very busy that day but that she will attend to his request the next day, and so not lose the opportunity to earn the money she has been offered.

If the chance of earning money or of avoiding some disaster are presented at the same time, the Sages affirm that the courtesan should concern herself with the money. But Vatsyayana points out that money has a limited value, while if an impending disaster is averted it does not usually return. The choice of the courtesan should be determined by the gravity or insignificance of the impending disaster.

The profits amassed by the richest and the best class of courtesans should be spent in the following way:

To construct temples, reservoirs and gardens;—To give a thousand cows to different Brahmins;—To perform religious ceremonies and celebrate festivals;—To accomplish the religious vows they have made.

The gains of other courtesans should be spent on the following things:

To buy a white robe to wear every day;—To buy enough food and drink so that she will not suffer from hunger or thirst;—To eat a perfumed 'pan' every day;—To buy gold-plated ornaments.

The Sages estimate that these expenses represent the profits made by the middle and lower-class prostitutes, but Vatsyayana disagrees and states that the income of these women cannot be calculated or fixed in any way, as it varies in each individual case with the place, the customs of the people, their physical appearance and many other factors.

If a courtesan wishes to prevent a man from propositioning another woman, or if she wishes to break up a liaison between two people, or deprive a woman of the income that she has earned, or if she feels that she can improve her position and better her status by making herself desirable to the clients of a particular woman, or if she wishes to procure a man's aid to avoid some disaster, or if she has sincerely fallen in love with him, or if she has seen some one wronged because of him, or if it is to repay a favor she has previously received, or if she wants to have intercourse with him simply because she desires him, in all these cases she should ask him for a small sum of money in a very informal and friendly way.

If a courtesan wishes to dispatch her present lover and take another, or if she has reason to believe that her lover will soon leave her to return to his wives, or that he has spent all his money and is completely bankrupt and his father, brother, or tutor will soon be coming to fetch the money back, or that her lover is about to lose his position, or is of an unstable temperament, in all these circumstances she should quickly try and acquire as much money as is possible from him.

On the other hand, if the courtesan thinks that her lover is about to receive beautiful gifts, or a post in the King's service, or inherit a large fortune, or that his ship full of riches is about to come into the harbor, or that he possesses great stocks of corn and other foodstuffs, or that if she does something for him it will not be effort wasted, or if he is always dependable, she will think of the future and live with him as if she were his wife.

> *In view of present benefits,*
> *In view of benefits to come,*
> *A courtesan should avoid men*
> *Who earn their bread by sweat*
> *Or who have grown hard and bitter*
> *Asking favors from the King.*
> *She should unite with rich and liberal lovers,*
> *And those whose anger might do her harm*

Even at the price of present sacrifice
She should give herself to generous and vigorous men
Who, once satisfied will repay her well
For some little service she may render them.

CHAPTER 7

On Gains, Losses, Doubts, and on the
different types of Prostitutes and Courtesans

It often happens that if one works hard for certain rewards one hopes to attain, the efforts are repaid by losses.

The reasons for these losses are:

Stupidity;—Excessive passion;—Excessive egotism;—Excessive pride;—Excessive simplicity;—Excessive confidence;—Excess of anger;—Laziness;—Carelessness;—Bad influences;—Unavoidable accidents.

The results of these losses are:

Expenses without any compensation;—Ruin of future welfare;— Loss of riches one was sure of earning;—Souring of the character; —Misanthropy;—A bad effect on the health;—Loss of hair, appetite and other accidents.

There are three kinds of profit: monetary profit, religious or spiritual profit and pleasurable profit. Similarly there are three kinds of losses: monetary loss, spiritual loss, and loss of pleasure or happiness.

If the moment one is engaged in acquiring certain profits other kinds of benefits also result, these are accessory profits.

If the profit is uncertain, the doubts entertained are known as Simple Doubts.

If, however, there is a doubt over which of two alternatives will succeed, it is known as a Mixed Doubt.

If one action has two results it is known as a Combination of Two Doubts.

And if the same action produces many results it is known as a Combination of Several Doubts.

Here are some examples:

1) If a courtesan is living with a rich and powerful personality

and thus acquires many riches, and at the same time the fact that she is constantly in contact with rich and powerful people enhances her chances for the future and also increases her wealth and so makes her universally desirable, it is known as riches accompanied by accessory profits.

2) If while living with a man, a courtesan gains money and wealth and nothing further it is an example of monetary profit accompanied by other benefits.

3) When a courtesan receives money from men other than her protector or lover, the result is that she risks the future well-being her lover's protection guarantees her; she risks disillusioning a man who sincerely loves her; she risks the scorn of everybody, and perhaps as a last hope, a liaison with a poor and wretched lover who will destroy all her chances in life. This is an example of a monetary profit accompanied by loss.

4) When a courtesan, at her own expense and without any immediate profit, forms a liaison with a powerful person or a miserly official with the intent of avoiding some danger or of removing some obstacle that stands in the way of some profit, this loss is an example of monetary loss accompanied by future profit.

5) When a courtesan is kind, even at her own expense, to a very miserly man, or one who is proud of his appearance, or ungrateful and accustomed to conquering women's hearts, and she receives no benefit from her action, this loss is known as a loss of riches without any gain.

6) When a courtesan is good to such men as described above and these men are the cruel and powerful favorites of the King, and she indulges them with no benefit for herself, because of the constant danger of being imprisoned or harmed if she displeases them, this loss is an example of a loss of wealth accompanied by other losses.

Thus the profits and losses as well as the spiritual and pleasurable gains and losses are explained to the reader who can then establish different combinations for himself.

There are also three kinds of doubts: doubts about riches, doubts of a spiritual nature, and doubts about pleasure.

For instance:

1) When a courtesan is not sure that a man can spend money on her, it is a doubt about riches.

2) When a courtesan has doubts about dismissing a lover she has ruined, as she took all his money within the first few weeks of intimacy, this is known as a spiritual or moral doubt.

3) When a courtesan is not physically satisfied by her lover and does not know if she will ever fully enjoy the relationship, as he

is always surrounded by his family or perhaps he is uncouth and of low parentage, it is known as a doubt about pleasure.

4) When a courtesan is worried that some powerful but evil person will harm her if she fails to show him the deference he desires, it is a doubt about the loss of riches.

5) When a courtesan cannot decide if she will lose religious merit if she abandons a man who is attached to her without according him the smallest favor, and thus bring sorrow on herself in this world and in the other, this is a doubt about the loss of religious merit.

6) If a courtesan fears that she might lose her lover's affection if she confides in him and reveals her love for him, and so lose her pleasure, it is known as a doubt on the loss of pleasure.

Mixed Doubts

1) Intercourse or a liaison with a stranger whose exact intentions are not known, and who may have been introduced by a lover or by a person in charge, could result in either a profit or a loss, and consequently this is known as a mixed doubt on the possible gain or loss of riches.

2) When a courtesan, to please a friend or through a feeling of pity, has intercourse with a Brahmin scholar, a religious student, a sacrificial priest, a devotee of a certain God or an ascetic, who could fall in love with her to the extent of dying from unrequited passion, it poses a problem of religious merit. And consequently it is called a mixed doubt on the gain or loss of religious merit.

3) If a courtesan relies completely on the descriptions furnished by others with regard to a man, and goes to find him without first making sure if he possesses all these good qualities, she may or may not find pleasure with him, depending on whether he is good or bad. This is known as a mixed doubt on the possibility of pleasure.

Uddalika describes the following as dual gains and losses:

1) If in living with a man a courtesan acquires both riches and pleasure simultaneously it is called a dual gain.

2) When a courtesan lives with a man and pays her own expenses and derives no benefits from him whatsoever, and then on top of that he takes back what he previously gave her, it is known as a dual loss.

3) When a courtesan is not sure that a new lover will become fond of her, or even if he does grow to love her whether he will

give her anything, it is known as a doubt on the possibility of a dual gain.

4) When a courtesan suspects that a former enemy, whom she is trying to seduce, may wish to harm her to satisfy an old grudge, or, even if he becomes fond of her, may in a moment of anger take back everything he has given her, it is known as a doubt on the possibility of a double loss.

Bhabravaya describes double gains and losses in the following way:

1) When a courtesan has a chance to earn money from a man she can go and visit as well as from one she cannot visit, it is a dual gain.

2) When a courtesan must spend a great deal of money to visit a man and yet risks losing an even greater sum if she does not visit him, it is known as a dual loss.

3) When a courtesan is not sure that the man she is going to see will give her anything without her having to spend something first, or if she abandons him, if she will receive something from another man, it is a doubt on the possibilities of a dual gain.

4) When a courtesan is afraid that in going to visit a former enemy he may take back all the gifts he once gave her, or on the other hand that if she does not visit him he may do her some terrible harm in revenge, it is known as a doubt on the possibility of a double loss.

By combining the above cases one obtains six kinds of results:

1) Gain on one side, loss on the other;—2) Gain on one side, doubt about gain on the other;—3) Gain on one side, doubt about loss on the other;—4) Loss on one side, doubt about gain on the other;—5) Doubt of gain on one side, doubt of loss on the other;—6) Doubt of loss on one side, loss on the other.

A courtesan, after having taken the above factors into consideration, and having asked the advice of her friends, must choose the path that will bring her the most profit, the best possibilities of financial wealth and protection against disasters. Religious merit and pleasure must also be studied in separate combinations, and then all three factors together, so as to arrive at the best possibility.

When a courtesan serves several men, she should extract financial profits from them as well as pleasure. At different festivals and during the spring, she should have her mother announce to different people that her daughter will give herself to the men who will satisfy this or that desire.

And when the young men hasten to her, delighted at the idea of an easy conquest, she must carefully consider what benefits she can get from each one of them.

The combinations of gains and losses on all sides are:

1) Gain on one side and loss on all the others;—2) Loss on one side and gain on all the others;—3) Gain on all sides;—4) Loss on all sides.

The different categories of courtesans who live off the acts of love are:

A brothel-keeper;—A servant;—A dissolute woman;—A dancer; —A worker;—A woman who has left her family;—A woman who lives off her beauty;—A professional courtesan.

All these different kinds of courtesans have relations with different kinds of men and they should always think of ways of deriving money and pleasure from them, and of separating from them, and of being reconciled again. They should always take into account the possible gains and losses, the accessory gains and losses and the various doubts that accompany these possibilities.

> *Men desire pleasure,*
> *Women money:*
> *They should therefore*
> *Study this section*
> *Which deals with the art*
> *Of making money.*
> *There are women who search for love,*
> *And there are those that search for money.*
> *The first will learn in the First Part*
> *All that concerns the science of love;*
> *The others can learn here*
> *The ways of making money*
> *As practiced by courtesans.*

PART SEVEN

SEDUCTION

CHAPTER 1

On Seduction and Aphrodisiacs

If, after trying all the suggestions mentioned in the preceding chapters, the desired object remains elusive, then the only solution possible is to turn to other and more artificial devices.

A good and healthy appearance, fine qualities, youth and broadmindedness are usually enough to make one appealing and attractive to others. If, however, a man or a woman lacks these qualities, he or she must not hesitate to have recourse to artificial methods to increase his or her charm and attraction.

Here are some recipes that have proved their worth through the ages:

1) An ointment composed of tabernamontana coronaria, of costus speciosus, and of flacourtia cataphracta can be used as a beauty cream.

2) To make oneself more appealing in the eyes of others, compose a fine powder of the above-mentioned plants and apply it to the wick of an oil lamp. The black pigment that results should then be applied to the eyelashes.

3) Oil of hogweed, echite outescens, sarina, yellow amaranth and a leaf of the nymphea rubbed on the body has the same effect.

4) A black pigment from the same plants also serves the same purpose.

5) To increase his powers of attraction a man should eat a powder composed of nelumbrium speciosum, blue lotus, mesna roxburghii, clarified butter, 'ghee' and honey.

6) Other remedies that achieve the same effect are:

An ointment composed of tabernamontana coronaria, and xanthochymus pictorius.

A peacock or hyena bone covered with gold plate and attached to the right arm.

A rosary made of shells which has been rendered powerful by certain incantations from the Arthvana Veda, or through the blessing of someone versed in the science of magic.

There are yet other methods to capture the affections.

If a man rubs his lingam with a mixture of the powder of cactus, black pepper and honey, and then indulges in sexual intercourse, his partner will submit completely to his will and will never desire union with another.

A mixture composed of the leaves of the vatodbhranta plant, of flowers thrown on a corpse awaiting cremation and a powder of peacock bones has the same result, as does the remains of a kite that has died a natural death mixed with cowach and honey. The plant emblica myrabola also possesses the same properties.

If the shoots of the plant vajnasubhi are cut into small pieces and mixed with arsenic and sulphur, then dried seven times, they are extremely powerful. When applied to the lingam they make it possible to subject any woman. If one is not sure of success, burn these same shoots at night and gaze into the smoke; if a golden moon can be seen behind the dark smoke it is an augur of certain success. Or, if one mixes this powder with the excreta of a monkey and then throws this compound over a young virgin, the maiden will never be given in marriage to anyone else.

A mixture of arrow-root and oil of mango which is left to ferment for six months in a hollow in the trunk of the 'sisu' tree also renders a man irresistible.

Another powerful medicine can be composed of camel bones dipped in the juice of the eclipta prostata. The bone should then be burnt and the black substance produced by the ashes should be carefully locked away in a box made of camel bones. If this mixture is applied with a camel hair brush along with some antimony on the eyelashes it bestows tremendous health-giving properties to the eyes, as it is very pure, and also ensures the conquest of any woman the user of this ointment may desire.

If a man desires to increase his sexual capacity both for his own pleasure and to ensure his success among women, there are many herbs and medicines which make this possible.

For instance, a man can greatly increase his sexual prowess by drinking milk mixed with sugar, the root of the plant uchchata, pepper, and liquorice. Also milk in which the testicles of a ram or a he-goat have been boiled produces the same effect. The juice of hedysrum gangeticum, kuili, kshirika, sansifiria, roxburhiana mixed with milk are also effective.

The ancient writers affirm that if a man grinds the grain and root of the trapa beipinosa, kasurika, jasmin and liquorice, and an onion, mixes the composition with milk, sugar, and ghee, then, after boiling the mixture, drinks it, he will be able to enjoy innumerable women without fatigue or a diminution of his powers.

Rice, sparrows' eggs boiled in milk with ghee and sugar produces the same result as does sesame seeds dipped in sparrows' eggs mixed with the fruit of the trapa bispinosa, kaskurika and then boiled in milk mixed with ghee, sugar, whole wheat flour and beans.

To preserve one's sexual powers until old age, a mixture of ghee, sugar, liquorice, mixed with equal quantities of the juice of fennel and milk and drunk daily will guarantee the preservation of one's sexual powers well into old age; for the burden of age is the lack of pleasure, and once this burden is removed man need not fear the approaching years.

Asparagus racemosus, shvadaushtra, gaduchi plants boiled with liquorice and milk, honey, and ghee in the spring have the same result.

But above all a healthy body is essential for an active life, and a mixture of ghee drunk every day during the spring acts as an excellent tonic.

The seed of the shvadaushtra plant and barley flowers mixed in equal quantities and eaten every morning when rising guarantees the same result.

The medicines that increase and preserve sexual strength are taught by medical science, the Vedas, initiates in the art of magic, and by relatives and close friends.

But above all, one should be very careful never to try any dubious experiments that could bring about a deterioration of the body. The death of household animals brings one in contact with impure objects.

The only successful methods are those which are healthy, efficacious, and approved by the Brahmins and friends.

Ways and means of exciting desires. Techniques for strengthening the lingam. Experiments and Recipes

If a man is unable to satisfy an Hastini or elephant woman, he must have recourse to other methods to give her the pleasure of sexual climax. He should caress the yoni with his hand or his fingers and not penetrate her until she is already very excited and the spasms of the orgasm have already commenced.

This is one of the ways to arouse desire in a woman.

Or he can make use of an apadravyas, which is a tubular object that is tied around the lingam to enlarge and lengthen it so that it can completely fill the yoni.

Bhabravaya states that these apadravyas should be fashioned out of gold, silver, brass, iron, ivory, buffalo horn, tin, lead or different kinds of wood. They should be soft, clean, capable of arousing the lingam to a greater effort and perfectly made so that they can fulfill their purpose without difficulty or discomfort.

But the author of this work is inclined to believe that each one should fashion the apadravyas to his own taste.

There are many different sorts of apadravyas:

1) The Brace (Valaya): this apadravya should be the same size as the lingam itself and the exterior surface should be rough.

2) The Pair (Sanghati): this is formed with two braces.

3) The Bracelet (Chudaka): this is composed of three or more braces joined together until they achieve the necessary length. There exists also a simpler form of bracelet, which is composed of an iron thread which is rolled around the lingam to support and strengthen it.

4) The Kantuka or Jalaka: this is a hollow tube, which has a rough exterior carved with soft bumps whose size has been estimated in relation to the dimensions of the yoni. The Kantuka is slipped around the lingam and attached to a belt.

If one is caught unprepared and does not have a Kantuka at hand, a similar device can be made out of the branch of an apple tree or the tubular stem of a gourd, or a reed softened with oils and extracts of plants, or even with pieces of polished wood attached together. All these devices should be attached to a belt like the orthodox Kantuka.

These devices can be used to cover and help the lingam, or in some cases as a substitute, as in the case of two women.

Among the people of the south there is a belief that one cannot enjoy truly intense sexual pleasure unless the lingam has been perforated.

Now if a young man wishes to try this method, he should pierce the lingam with a very sharp instrument and then sit in water until the bleeding has stopped. The same evening he should indulge in a very active form of sexual intercourse so that the hole can be cleansed. After this, he should continue to wash the hole with various liquids and if he wishes he can make the hole larger by inserting reeds which will gradually enlarge the orifice. One can also wash the wound with a mixture of honey mixed with liquorice, and anoint the hole with a little oil.

In this hole across the lingam one can insert many kinds of apadravyas such as: the Round (round on one side);—the wooden mortar;—the flower;—the bracelet;—the heron's bone;—the elephant's goad;—the eight balls;—the lock of hair;—and other such objects, which are named after the shapes and purposes they serve. All these apadravyas should possess a rough exterior which adds to the efficacy of their use.

But there are also various ways of naturally strengthening the lingam.

One of the best and most durable methods has long been practiced by the Dravidians. The man should rub his lingam with the hairs of certain insects which live in trees; then he should grease the organ for ten nights and then rub it once again with the fine hairs of these insects. He should continue this treatment until the lingam gradually begins to swell. Then he should lie in a hammock and allow his lingam to hang down through a hole he has pierced in the swing. After some time he should soothe the pain caused by the swelling by applying cooling ointments to the organ. This swelling, which is known as suka, endures for a lifetime.

If one rubs the lingam with a mixture of physalis flexuosa, shavarakandaka, jalasuka, the fruit of the egg-plant, butter made of buffalo's milk, the plant hasticharma and the juice of the plant vajrarasa, the enlargement obtained will last for one month.

On the other hand, if one boils the above ingredients in oil and then rubs this mixture on the organ the swelling thus obtained will last for about six months.

A mixture of oil boiled with pomegranate seeds, cucumber, the juice of the plant valuka, egg-plant and hasticharma is also effective and gives a gradual growth.

But there are still other methods whose success has been guaranteed by repeated experiment by wise and learned men.

If a man mixes the powder of a milk-giving hedge plant and

the plant kantala with the excreta of a monkey and the ground root of the plant lanjalika, and throws this mixture on a woman she will never love anyone else.

If on the other hand, a man makes a sort of jelly with the juices of the fruit cassia fistula and eugenie jambolina and mixes in the powder of the plants soma, vernonia anthelmintica, eclipta prostata, lahopa-juihirka, and applies this mixture to the yoni of a woman with whom he is about to have intercourse, he will instantly cease to love her.

The same effect can be achieved if a man has intercourse with a woman who has taken a bath in buffalo milk mixed with the powder from the plants yellow amaranth, gopalika and banapadika.

If an ointment composed of the flowers nauclea cadamba and of eugenia jambolina is applied to the yoni by a woman, it will make her husband detest her. Garlands woven with the same flowers have the same effect.

An ointment composed of the fruit of the asteracantha longifolia contracts the yoni of a 'Hastini' or Elephant woman, but this contraction only lasts one night.

On the other hand, a cream composed of the ground roots of the nelubrium speciosum, of the blue lotus, physalis flexuosa mixed with ghee and honey dilates the yoni of a 'Migri' or doe woman.

The fruit emblica myrabolans soaked in the milk of the plant soma, the calotropi gigante, and in the juice of the fruit vernonia anthelmintica, dyes the hair white.

While the juice of the roots of the plant madayavtaka, the yellow amaranth, the anjanika, the clitoria ternatea and the plant shlasknaparni if employed as a lotion, makes the hair grow.

A cream composed of the above ingredients boiled in oil, and then rubbed on the scalp, darkens the hair and strengthens the falling hairs and makes them grow.

If one dips lacquer seven times in the seed of the testicles of a white horse and then applies this mixture on reddened lips, the lips will instantly turn white.

The natural color of the lips will return with the use of the plant madayantika and other herbs.

A woman who hears a man playing a reed-pipe that has previously been dipped in a mixture of the herbs hahupadika, tabernamontana coronaria, costus speciosus, pinus deodora and euphorbia antiquorum, vajra and kantaka, becomes his slave for life.

If one mixes the fruit of the prickly apple into food, the result is poisonous.

If one mixes water with oil and with the ashes of certain herbs this water takes on the color and texture of milk.

If one grinds a mixture of yellow myrabolans pig plums, the plants shrawana and priyangu, and applies this powder on iron vases, the vases turn red.

If one lights a lamp whose wick is made out of snake skin, and fills it with the oil of the above-mentioned plants, and then places a piece of wood beside the flame, the wood will itself resemble a snake.

The milk of a white cow who has a white calf nestling beside her possesses excellent properties, and, if drunk, lengthens one's life and brings fame and fortune.

The blessings given by venerable Brahmins have the same effect.

CONCLUSION

Thus I have condensed the Science of Love into a few words, after having read the works of ancient writers and observed and studied the various paths to pleasure mentioned therein.

Those who fully understand the principle of this science act in accordance with the rules of Dharma, Artha and Kama, consult their own experience, and the teachings of those older than themselves, and do not act impulsively following their fancies down destructive paths. Certain practices in the science of love that I have mentioned in the course of this book with my own authority as author I have condemned and prohibited immediately afterwards.

An act should never be excused on the grounds that science authorizes it, because one must bear in mind that these rules are applicable only in particular cases. After having read Bhabravaya and other ancient writers, and having studied the meaning of the rules laid down by them, Vatsyayana has composed the Kama Sutra in perfect accordance with the Holy Scriptures for the benefit of the world, while he himself led the life of a student of religion and was totally absorbed in the contemplation of God.

This work was not intended as an instrument to satisfy the carnal desires common to all men. But a person who possesses the real principles of this science cultivates his Dharma, Artha and Kama with care, and taking into consideration the traditions and ways of society, is able to develop a complete control over his senses.

In short, an intelligent person who develops Dharma and Artha as well as Kama without becoming the slave of his passions, succeeds in everything he undertakes.